AS-Level
Physics

The Revision Guide

Editors:
Amy Boutal, Simon Little, Julie Wakeling, Sarah Williams

Contributors
Tony Alldridge, Jane Cartwright, Peter Cecil, Peter Clarke, Mark A. Edwards, Barbara Mascetti, John Myers, Zoe Nye, Andy Williams

Proofreaders:
Mark A. Edwards, Ian Francis, Glenn Rogers

Published by Coordination Group Publications Ltd.

This book covers:

AQA A
Edexcel
OCR A
OCR B (Advancing Physics)

There are notes on the pages to tell you which bits you need for your syllabus.

The whole of Section Seven is for **AQA A** only.

Data used to construct stopping distance diagram on page 26 from the Highway Code.
Reproduced under the terms of the Click-Use Licence.

With thanks to Science Photo Library for permission to reproduce the photographs used on pages 38 and 39.

With thanks to Jan Greenway for the copyright research.

ISBN: 978 1 84762 130 6

Groovy website: www.cgpbooks.co.uk
Jolly bits of clipart from CorelDRAW®
Printed by Elanders Hindson Ltd, Newcastle upon Tyne.

Contents

The Scientific Process

*'How Science Works' is all about the scientific process — how we develop and test scientific ideas.
It's what scientists do all day, every day (well, except at coffee time — never come between a scientist and their coffee).*

Scientists Come Up with **Theories** — Then **Test Them**...

Science tries to explain **how** and **why** things happen — it **answers questions**. It's all about seeking and gaining **knowledge** about the world around us. Scientists do this by **asking** questions and **suggesting** answers and then **testing** them, to see if they're correct — this is the **scientific process**.

1) **Ask** a question — make an **observation** and ask **why or how** it happens.
   E.g. what is the nature of light?

2) **Suggest** an answer, or part of an answer, by forming:
   - a **theory** (a possible **explanation** of the observations)
     e.g. light is a wave.
   - a **model** (a **simplified picture** of what's physically going on)

3) Make a **prediction** or **hypothesis** — a **specific testable statement**, based on the theory, about what will happen in a test situation.
   E.g. light should interfere and diffract.

4) Carry out a **test** — to provide **evidence** that will support the prediction, or help disprove it. E.g. Young's double-slit experiment.

The evidence supported Quentin's Theory of Flammable Burps.

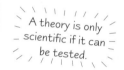

A theory is only scientific if it can be tested.

...Then They **Tell** Everyone About Their **Results**...

The results are **published** — scientists need to let others know about their work. Scientists publish their results in **scientific journals**. These are just like normal magazines, only they contain **scientific reports** (called papers) instead of the latest celebrity gossip.

1) Scientific reports are similar to the **lab write-ups** you do in school. And just as a lab write-up is **reviewed** (marked) by your teacher, reports in scientific journals undergo **peer review** before they're published.

2) The report is sent out to **peers** — other scientists that are experts in the **same area**. They examine the data and results, and if they think that the conclusion is reasonable it's **published**. This makes sure that work published in scientific journals is of a **good standard**.

3) But peer review **can't guarantee** the science is **correct** — other scientists still need to **reproduce** it.

4) Sometimes **mistakes** are made and bad work is published. Peer review **isn't perfect** but it's probably the best way for scientists to self-regulate their work and to publish **quality reports**.

...Then **Other Scientists** Will **Test** the Theory Too

Other scientists read the published theories and results, and try to **test the theory** themselves. This involves:
- Repeating the **exact same experiments**.
- Using the theory to make **new predictions** and then testing them with **new experiments**.

If the **Evidence** Supports a Theory, It's **Accepted** — for Now

1) If all the experiments in all the world provide evidence to back it up, the theory is thought of as **scientific 'fact'** (for now).

2) But they never become **totally undisputable** fact. Scientific **breakthroughs or advances** could provide new ways to question and test the theory, which could lead to **new evidence** that **conflicts** with the current evidence. Then the testing starts all over again...

And this, my friend, is the **tentative nature of scientific knowledge** — it's always **changing** and **evolving**.

The Scientific Process

So scientists need evidence to back up their theories. They get it by carrying out experiments, and when that's not possible they carry out studies. But why bother with science at all? We want to know as much as possible so we can use it to try and improve our lives (and because we're nosey).

Evidence Comes From Controlled Lab Experiments...

1) Results from **controlled experiments** in **laboratories** are great.
2) A lab is the easiest place to **control variables** so that they're all **kept constant** (except for the one you're investigating).

> For example, finding the resistance of a piece of material by altering the voltage across the material and measuring the current flowing through it (see p. 50). All other variables need to be kept the same, e.g. the dimensions of the piece of material being tested, as they may also affect its resistance.

... That You can Draw Meaningful Conclusions From

1) You always need to make your experiments as **controlled** as possible so you can be confident that any effects you see are linked to the variable you're changing.
2) If you do find a relationship, you need to be careful what you conclude. You need to decide whether the effect you're seeing is **caused** by changing a variable, or whether the two are just **correlated**.

"Right Geoff, you can start the experiment now... I've stopped time..."

Society Makes Decisions Based on Scientific Evidence

1) Lots of scientific work eventually leads to **important discoveries** or breakthroughs that could **benefit humankind**.
2) These results are **used by society** (that's you, me and everyone else) to **make decisions** — about the way we live, what we eat, what we drive, etc.
3) All sections of society use scientific evidence to make decisions, e.g. politicians use it to devise policies and individuals use science to make decisions about their own lives.

Other factors can **influence** decisions about science or the way science is used:

Economic factors
- Society has to consider the **cost** of implementing changes based on scientific conclusions — e.g. the cost of reducing the UK's carbon emissions to limit the human contribution to **global warming**.
- Scientific research is often **expensive**. E.g. in areas such as astronomy, the Government has to **justify** spending money on a new telescope rather than pumping money into, say, the **NHS** or **schools**.

Social factors
- **Decisions** affect **people's lives** — e.g. when looking for a site to build a **nuclear power station**, you need to consider how it would affect the lives of the people in the **surrounding area**.

Environmental factors
- Many scientists suggest that building **wind farms** would be a **cheap** and **environmentally friendly** way to generate electricity in the future. But some people think that because **wind turbines** can **harm wildlife** such as birds and bats, other methods of generating electricity should be used.

So there you have it — how science works...

Hopefully these pages have given you a nice intro to how science works, e.g. what scientists do to provide you with 'facts'. You need to understand this, as you're expected to know how science works yourself — for the exam and for life.

Scalars and Vectors

These pages are for AQA A Unit 2, Edexcel Unit 1, OCR A Unit 1 and OCR B Unit 2.

Mechanics is one of those things that you either love or hate. I won't tell you which side of the fence I'm on.

Scalars Only Have Size, but Vectors Have Size and Direction

1) A **scalar** has **no direction** — it's **just an amount** of something, like the **mass** of a **sack of meaty dog food**.

2) A **vector** has magnitude (**size**) and **direction** — like the **speed and direction** of next door's **cat** running away.

3) **Force** and **velocity** are both **vectors** — you need to know **which way** they're going as well as **how big** they are.

4) Here are a few examples to get you started:

Scalars	Vectors
mass, temperature, time, length, speed, energy	displacement, force, velocity, acceleration, momentum

Adding Vectors Involves Pythagoras and Trigonometry

Adding two or more vectors is called finding the **resultant** of them.
You find the resultant of two vectors by drawing them '**tip-to-tail**'.

Example   Jemima goes for a walk. She walks 3 m North and 4 m East. She has walked 7 m but she isn't 7 m from her starting point. Find the magnitude and direction of her displacement.

First, draw the vectors **tip-to-tail**. Then draw a line from the **tail** of the first vector to the **tip** of the last vector to give the **resultant**: Because the vectors are at right angles, you get the **magnitude** of the resultant using Pythagoras:

$R^2 = 3^2 + 4^2 = 25$

So $R = 5$ m

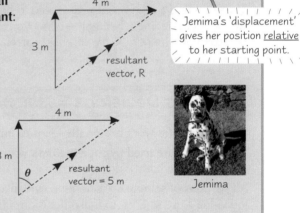

Jemima's 'displacement' gives her position <u>relative</u> to her starting point.

Now find the **bearing** of Jemima's new position from her original position.

You use the triangle again, but this time you need to use trigonometry. You know the opposite and the adjacent sides, so you need to use:

$\tan \theta = 4/3$

$\theta = 53.1°$ Trig's really useful in mechanics — so make sure you're completely okay with it. Remember SOH CAH TOA.

Jemima

Use the Same Method for Resultant Forces or Velocities

If the vectors aren't at right angles, you'll need to do a scale drawing.

Always start by drawing a diagram.

Example

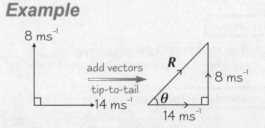

You know the resultant force is at 45° to the horizontal (since both forces are the same size).

So all you need to do is use Pythagoras:

$R^2 = 2^2 + 2^2 = 8$

which gives $R = 2.83$ N at 45° to the horizontal.

Don't forget to take the square root.

Example

Start with: $R^2 = 14^2 + 8^2 = 260$

so you get: $R = 16.1$ ms^{-1}.

Then: $\tan \theta = 8/14 = 0.5714$

$\theta = 29.7°$

Scalars and Vectors

Sometimes you have to do it backwards.

It's Useful to Split a **Vector** into **Horizontal** and **Vertical Components**

This is the opposite of finding the resultant — you start from the resultant vector and split it into two **components** at right angles to each other. You're basically **working backwards** from the examples on the other page.

Resolving a vector v into horizontal and vertical components

You get the **horizontal** component v_x like this:

$$\cos \theta = v_x / v$$

$$\boxed{v_x = v \cos \theta}$$

...and the **vertical** component v_y like this:

$$\sin \theta = v_y / v$$

$$\boxed{v_y = v \sin \theta}$$

See pages 18 and 19 for more on resolving.

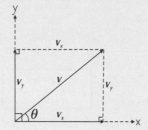

θ is measured anticlockwise from the horizontal.

Example

Charley's amazing floating home is travelling at a speed of 5 ms⁻¹ at an angle of 60° up from the horizontal. Find the vertical and horizontal components.

Charley's mobile home was the envy of all his friends.

The **horizontal** component v_x is:

$v_x = v \cos \theta = \mathbf{5 \cos 60°} = 2.5$ ms⁻¹

The vertical component v_y is:

$v_y = v \sin \theta = \mathbf{5 \sin 60°} = 4.33$ ms⁻¹

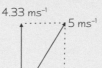

Resolving is dead useful because the two components of a vector **don't affect each other**. This means you can deal with the two directions **completely separately**.

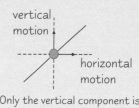

Only the vertical component is affected by gravity.

Practice Questions

Q1 Explain the difference between a scalar quantity and a vector quantity.

Q2 Jemima has gone for a swim in a river which is flowing at 0.35 ms⁻¹. She swims at 0.18 ms⁻¹ at right angles to the current. Show that her resultant velocity is 0.39 ms⁻¹ at an angle of 27.2° to the current.

Q3 Jemima is pulling on her lead with a force of 40 N at an angle of 26° below the horizontal. Show that the horizontal component of this force is about 36 N.

Exam Questions

Q1 The wind is creating a horizontal force of 20 N on a falling rock of weight 75 N. Calculate the magnitude and direction of the resultant force. [2 marks]

Q2 A glider is travelling at a velocity of 20.0 ms⁻¹ at an angle of 15° below the horizontal. Find the horizontal and vertical components of the glider's velocity. [2 marks]

His Dark Vectors Trilogy — displacement, velocity and acceleration...

Well there's nothing like starting the book on a high. And this is nothing like... yes, OK. Ahem. Well, good evening folks. I'll mostly be handing out useful information in boxes like this. But I thought I'd not rush into it, so this one's totally useless.

Motion with Constant Acceleration

These pages are for AQA A Unit 2, Edexcel Unit 1, OCR A Unit 1 and OCR B Unit 2.

Uniform Acceleration is Constant Acceleration

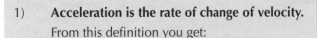

Acceleration could mean a change in speed or direction or both.

Uniform means **constant** here. It's nothing to do with what you wear.

There are **four main equations** that you use to solve problems involving **uniform acceleration**.

You need to be able to use them, and if you're doing *OCR A* or *OCR B* you need to know how they're **derived**.

1) **Acceleration is the rate of change of velocity.**
From this definition you get:

$$a = \frac{(v-u)}{t} \quad \text{so} \quad \boxed{v = u + at}$$

where:
u = initial velocity a = acceleration
v = final velocity t = time taken

2) **s = average velocity × time**
If acceleration is constant, the average velocity is just the average of the initial and final velocities, so:

$$\boxed{s = \frac{(u+v)}{2} \times t} \quad s = \text{displacement}$$

3) Substitute the expression for v from equation 1 into equation 2 to give:

$$s = \frac{(u+u+at) \times t}{2} = \frac{2ut + at^2}{2} \qquad \boxed{s = ut + \tfrac{1}{2}at^2}$$

4) You can **derive** the fourth equation from equations **1** and **2**:

Use equation **1** in the form:
$$a = \frac{v-u}{t}$$

Multiply both sides by s, where:
$$s = \frac{(u+v)}{2} \times t$$

This gives us:
$$as = \frac{(v-u)}{t} \times \frac{(u+v)t}{2}$$

The t's on the right cancel, so:
$$2as = (v-u)(v+u)$$
$$2as = v^2 - uv + uv - u^2$$

so:
$$\boxed{v^2 = u^2 + 2as}$$

Example

A tile falls from a roof 25 m high. Calculate its speed when it hits the ground and how long it takes to fall. Take $g = 9.8$ ms^{-2}.

First of all, write out what you know:

$s = 25$ m

$u = 0$ ms^{-1} since the tile's stationary to start with

$a = 9.8$ ms^{-2} due to gravity

$v = ?$ $t = ?$

Usually you take upwards as the positive direction. In this question it's probably easier to take downwards as positive, so you get $g = +9.8$ ms^{-2} instead of $g = -9.8$ ms^{-2}.

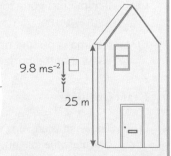

9.8 ms^{-2}

25 m

Then, choose an equation with only **one unknown quantity**.
So start with $v^2 = u^2 + 2as$

$v^2 = 0 + 2 \times 9.8 \times 25$

$v^2 = 490$

$v = 22.1$ ms^{-1}

Now, find t using:

$s = ut + \tfrac{1}{2}at^2$

$25 = 0 + \tfrac{1}{2} \times 9.8 \times t^2$

$t^2 = \frac{25}{4.9}$

Final answers:

$t = 2.3$ s

$v = 22.1$ ms^{-1}

Motion with Constant Acceleration

Example

A car accelerates steadily from rest at a rate of 4.2 ms⁻² for 6 seconds.
a)   Calculate the final speed.
b)   Calculate the distance travelled in 6 seconds.

4.2 ms⁻²

Remember — always start by writing down what you know.

a) $a = 4.2$ ms⁻²   choose the right equation… $v = u + at$
      $u = 0$ ms⁻¹ $v = 0 + 4.2 \times 6$
      $t = 6$ s   *Final answer:* $v = 25.2$ ms⁻¹
      $v = ?$

b) $s = ?$ you can use: $s = \dfrac{(u+v)t}{2}$ or: $s = ut + \tfrac{1}{2}at^2$
      $t = 6$ s
      $u = 0$ ms⁻¹
      $a = 4.2$ ms⁻² $s = \dfrac{(0+25.2)\times 6}{2}$ $s = 0 + \tfrac{1}{2} \times 4.2 \times (6)^2$
      $v = 25.2$ ms⁻¹

                          Final answer: $s = 75.6$ m $s = 75.6$ m

You Have to **Learn** the Constant Acceleration **Equations**

Make sure you learn the equations. There are only four of them and these questions are always
dead easy marks in the exam, so you'd be daft as a brush in daft town not to learn them...

Practice Questions

Q1   Write out the four constant acceleration equations.
Q2   Show how the equation s = ut + ½ at² can be derived.

Exam Questions

Q1   A skydiver jumps from an aeroplane when it is flying horizontally. She accelerates due to gravity for 5 s.
      (a) Calculate her maximum vertical velocity. (Assume no air resistance.)   [2 marks]
      (b) How far does she fall in this time?   [2 marks]

Q2   A motorcyclist slows down uniformly as he approaches a red light. He takes 3.2 seconds to
      come to a halt and travels 40 m in this time.
      (a) How fast was he travelling initially?   [2 marks]
      (b) Calculate his acceleration. (N.B. a negative value shows a deceleration.)   [2 marks]

Q3   A stream provides a constant acceleration of 6 ms⁻². A toy boat is pushed directly against the current
      from a point 1.2 m upstream from a small waterfall, then released. Just before it reaches the waterfall,
      it is travelling at a speed of 5 ms⁻¹.
      (a) Find the initial velocity of the boat.   [2 marks]
      (b) What is the maximum distance upstream from the waterfall the boat reaches?   [2 marks]

Constant acceleration — it'll end in tears...

*If a question talks about "uniform" or "constant" acceleration, it's a dead giveaway they want you to use one of these
equations. The tricky bit is working out which one to use — start every question by writing out what you know and
what you need to know. That makes it much easier to see which equation you need. To be sure. Arrr.*

Free Fall

These pages are for AQA A Unit 2, Edexcel Unit 1, OCR A Unit 1 and OCR B Unit 2.

So, how do you work this parachute thing agaiAAAAAaaaaaarrrrrgggghhhhhhhhhhhhhh...

Free Fall is when there's Only **Gravity** and Nothing Else

Free fall is defined as "the motion of an object undergoing an acceleration of '**g**'".
You need to remember:

1) Acceleration is a **vector quantity** — and '**g**' acts **vertically downwards**.

2) Unless you're given a different value, take the magnitude of **g** as **9.81 ms⁻²**, though it varies slightly at different points on the Earth's surface.

3) The **only force** acting on an object in free fall is its **weight**.

4) Objects can have an initial velocity in any direction and still undergo **free fall** as long as the **force** providing the initial velocity is **no longer acting**.

You Can **Measure g** by using an Object in **Free Fall**

Measuring g is for OCR A only.

You don't have to do it this way — but if you don't know a method of measuring **g** already, learn this one.

You need to be able to:

1) **Sketch** a diagram of the **apparatus**.
2) **Describe** the **method**.
3) **List** the **measurements** you make.
4) **Explain** how '**g**' is **calculated**.
5) Be aware of sources of **error**.

Another gravity experiment.

Experiment to Measure the Acceleration Due to Gravity

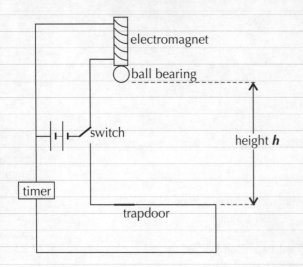

In this experiment you have to assume that the effect of air resistance on the ball bearing is negligible and that the magnetism of the electromagnet decays instantly.

The Method:

1) Measure the height **h** from the **bottom** of the ball bearing to the **trapdoor**.

2) Flick the switch to simultaneously start the timer and disconnect the electromagnet, releasing the ball bearing.

3) The ball bearing falls, knocking the trapdoor down and breaking the circuit — which stops the timer.

Use the time **t** measured by the timer, and the height **h** that the ball bearing has fallen, to calculate a value for **g**, using $h = \frac{1}{2}gt^2$ (see next page for more on acceleration formulas).

The most significant source of error in this experiment will be in the measurement of **h**.
Using a ruler, you'll have an uncertainty of about 1 mm.
This dwarfs any error from switch delay or air resistance.

Free Fall

You can Just Replace a with g in the Equations of Motion

You need to be able to work out **speeds**, **distances** and **times** for objects in **free fall**. Since g is a **constant acceleration** you can use the **constant acceleration equations**. But g acts downwards, so you need to be careful about directions.

To make it clear, there's a sign convention: **upwards is positive**, **downwards is negative**.

> ### Sign Conventions — Learn Them:
> g is always <u>downwards</u> so it's <u>usually negative</u>   t is <u>always positive</u>
> u and v can be either <u>positive or negative</u>   s can be either <u>positive or negative</u>

Case 1: No initial velocity (it just falls)

Initial velocity $u = 0$
Acceleration $a = g = -9.81$ ms^{-2}
So the constant acceleration equations become: $\Longrightarrow$

$$v = gt \qquad v^2 = 2gs$$
$$s = \frac{1}{2}gt^2 \qquad s = \frac{vt}{2}$$

Case 2: An initial velocity upwards (it's thrown up into the air)

The constant acceleration equations are just as normal,
but with $a = g = -9.81$ ms^{-2}

Case 3: An initial velocity downwards (it's thrown down)

Example: Alex throws a stone down a cliff. She gives it a downwards velocity of 2 ms^{-1}. It takes 3 s to reach the water below. How high is the cliff?

1) You know $u = -2$ ms^{-1}, $a = g = -9.81$ ms^{-2} and $t = 3$ s. You need to find **s**. — *s will be negative because the stone ends up further down than it started*

2) Use $s = ut + \frac{1}{2}gt^2 = (-2 \times 3) + \left(\frac{1}{2} \times -9.81 \times 3^2\right) = -50.1$ m. **The cliff is 50.1 m high.**

Practice Questions

Q1 What is the value of the acceleration of a free-falling object?
Q2 What is the initial velocity of an object which is dropped?

Exam Questions

Q1 A student has designed a device to estimate the value of 'g'. It consists of two narrow strips of card joined by a piece of transparent plastic. The student drops the device through a light gate connected to a computer. As the device falls, the strips of card break the light beam.
(a) What three pieces of data will the student need from the computer to estimate 'g'? [3 marks]
(b) Explain how the measurements from the light gate can be used to estimate 'g'. [3 marks]
(c) Give one reason why the student's value of 'g' will not be entirely accurate. [1 mark]

Q2 Charlene is bouncing on a trampoline. She reaches her highest point a height of 5 m above the trampoline.
(a) Calculate the speed with which she leaves the trampoline surface. [2 marks]
(b) How long does it take her to reach the highest point? [2 marks]
(c) What will her velocity be as she lands back on the trampoline? [2 marks]

It's not the falling that hurts — it's the being pelted with rotten vegetables... okay, okay...

The hardest bit with free fall questions is getting your signs right. Draw yourself a little diagram before you start doing any calculations, and label it with what you know and what you want to know. That can help you get the signs straight in your head. It also helps the person marking your paper if it's clear what your sign convention is. Always good.

Free Fall and Projectile Motion

Page 10 is just for AQA A Unit 2 and OCR A Unit 1. Page 11 is <u>also</u> for Edexcel Unit 1 and OCR B Unit 2.

What goes up, must come down — but no one really questioned why until Aristotle. He thought he knew... but then Galileo and Newton sure showed him...

Aristotle — *Heavy* Objects Fall *Quicker* than *Lighter* objects

1) **Aristotle** was an ancient Greek philosopher who sat around thinking about pretty much everything, including the **joys of Physics**.

2) He used **reasoning** to try and work out how the world worked from **everyday** observations.

3) One of his famous theories was that if **two objects** of **different mass** are dropped from the **same height**, the **heavier** object would always hit the ground **before** the lighter object.

Trev was counting... there was no way Tez took longer to hit the ground than him.

Galileo — *All* Objects in Free Fall Accelerate *Uniformly*

1) Galileo thought that **all objects accelerate towards the ground at the same rate** — so objects with different weights dropped from the same height should hit the ground at the **same time**.

2) Not only that, but he reckoned the reason objects didn't seem to do this was because of the effect of **air resistance** on different objects.

3) Believe it or not, scientists don't think Galileo chucked stuff from the top of the Leaning Tower of Pisa to test this theory. Instead he did an even more exciting experiment — he.. er... rolled balls down a slope.

Example: The Inclined Plane Experiment

1) Handy things like stop clocks and light gates hadn't been invented, so Galileo had to find a way of slowing down the free fall of an object without otherwise affecting to have any chance of showing it accelerating.

2) Ta da — the inclined plane experiment was born. Galileo found that by rolling a ball down a **smooth** groove in an inclined plane, he **reduced** the effect of **air resistance** while slowing the ball's fall at the same time.

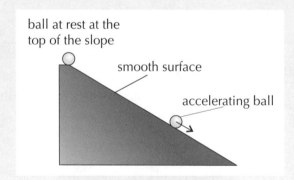

ball at rest at the top of the slope

smooth surface

accelerating ball

3) He timed how long it took the ball to roll from the top of the slope to the bottom using a water clock.

4) By rolling the ball along different fractions of the total length of the slope, he found that the distance the ball travelled was proportional to the square of the time taken. The ball was **accelerating** at a **constant rate**.

5) In the end it took Newton to bring it all together and explain why **all** free-falling objects have the **same acceleration** (see page 22).

Galileo *Tested* his *Theories* using *Experiments*

1) Not only did Galileo disagree with Aristotle on almost everything, he liked to shout it from the rooftops. He not only managed to insult other philosophers at the time, but the Pope and the entire Catholic church too — which got him in a whole **load of trouble**.

2) Even though he was so unpopular, Galileo's theories eventually overturned Aristotle's and became **generally accepted**. He wasn't the first person to question Aristotle, but his success was down to the **systematic** and **rigorous experiments** he used to **test** his theories. These experiments could be repeated and the results described **mathematically** and compared.

3) It's not much different in science now. You make a prediction and test it — the more **scientific evidence** that supports your theory, the more **accepted** it becomes.

Free Fall and Projectile Motion

Any object given an initial velocity and then left to move freely under gravity is a projectile.
If you're doing AS Maths, you've got all this to look forward to in M1 as well, quite likely. Fun for all the family.

You have to think of **Horizontal** and **Vertical** Motion **Separately**

Example
Sharon fires a scale model of a TV talent show presenter horizontally with a velocity of 100 ms^{-1} from 1.5 m above the ground. How long does it take to hit the ground, and how far does it travel? Assume the model acts as a particle, the ground is horizontal and there is no air resistance.

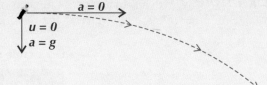

Think about vertical motion first:
1) It's **constant acceleration** under gravity...
2) You know $u = 0$ (no vertical velocity at first), $s = -1.5$ m and $a = g = -9.81$ ms^{-2}. You need to find t.
3) Use $s = \frac{1}{2}gt^2 \Rightarrow t = \sqrt{\frac{2s}{g}} = \sqrt{\frac{2 \times -1.5}{-9.81}} = 0.55$ s
4) So the model hits the ground after **0.55** seconds.

Then do the horizontal motion:
1) The horizontal motion isn't affected by gravity or any other force, so it moves at a **constant speed**.
2) That means you can just use good old **speed = distance / time**.
3) Now $v_h = 100$ ms^{-1}, $t = 0.55$ s and $a = 0$. You need to find s_h.
4) $s_h = v_h t = 100 \times 0.55 = \underline{55 \text{ m}}$

Where v_h is the horizontal velocity, and s_h is the horizontal distance travelled (rather than the height fallen).

It's **Slightly Trickier** if it **Starts Off** at an **Angle**

If something's projected at an angle (like, say, a javelin) you start off with both horizontal and vertical velocity:

Method:
1) Resolve the initial velocity into horizontal and vertical components.
2) Use the vertical component to work out how long it's in the air and/or how high it goes.
3) Use the horizontal component to work out how far it goes while it's in the air.

Practice Questions

Q1 What is the initial vertical velocity for an object projected horizontally with a velocity of 5 ms^{-1}?
Q2 How does the horizontal velocity of a free-falling object change with time?
Q3 What is the main reason Galileo's ideas became generally accepted in place of Aristotle's?

Exam Questions

Q1 Jason stands on a vertical cliff edge throwing stones into the sea below.
He throws a stone horizontally with a velocity of 20 ms^{-1}, 560 m above sea level.
(a) How long does it take for the stone to hit the water from leaving Jason's hand?
Use g = 9.81 ms^{-2} and ignore air resistance.   [2 marks]
(b) Find the distance of the stone from the base of the cliff when it hits the water.   [2 marks]

Q2 Robin fires an arrow into the air with a vertical velocity of 30 ms^{-1}, and a horizontal velocity of 20 ms^{-1}, from 1 m above the ground. Find the maximum height from the ground reached by his arrow.
Use g = 9.81 ms^{-2} and ignore air resistance.   [3 marks]

So it's this "Galileo" geezer who's to blame for my practicals...

Ah, the ups and downs and er... acrosses of life. Make sure you're happy splitting an object's motion into horizontal and vertical bits — it comes up all over mechanics. Hmmm... I wonder what Galileo would be proudest of, insisting on the systematic, rigorous experimental method on which modern science hangs... or getting in a Queen song? Magnificooooooo...

Displacement-Time Graphs

These pages are for *AQA A Unit 2, Edexcel Unit 1, OCR A Unit 1* and *OCR B Unit 2*.

Drawing graphs by hand — oh joy. You'd think examiners had never heard of the graphical calculator.
Ah well, until they manage to drag themselves out of the dark ages, you'll just have to grit your teeth and get on with it.

Acceleration Means a Curved Displacement-Time Graph

A graph of displacement against time for an **accelerating object** always produces a **curve**.
If the object is accelerating at a **uniform rate**, then the **rate of change** of the **gradient** will be constant.

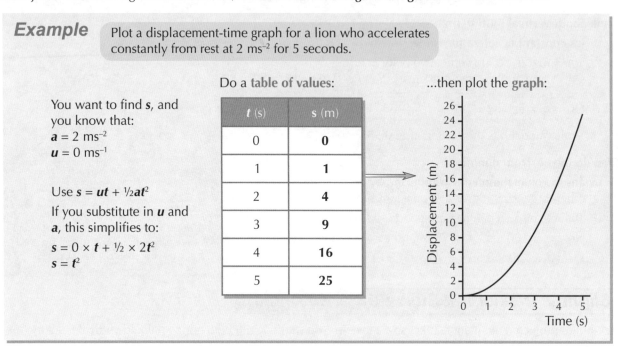

Example Plot a displacement-time graph for a lion who accelerates constantly from rest at 2 ms⁻² for 5 seconds.

You want to find **s**, and you know that:
$a = 2$ ms^{-2}
$u = 0$ ms^{-1}

Use $s = ut + \frac{1}{2}at^2$
If you substitute in **u** and **a**, this simplifies to:
$s = 0 \times t + \frac{1}{2} \times 2t^2$
$s = t^2$

Do a **table of values**:

t (s)	s (m)
0	0
1	1
2	4
3	9
4	16
5	25

...then plot the **graph**:

Different Accelerations Have Different Gradients

In the example above, if the lion has a **different acceleration** it'll change the **gradient** of the curve like this:

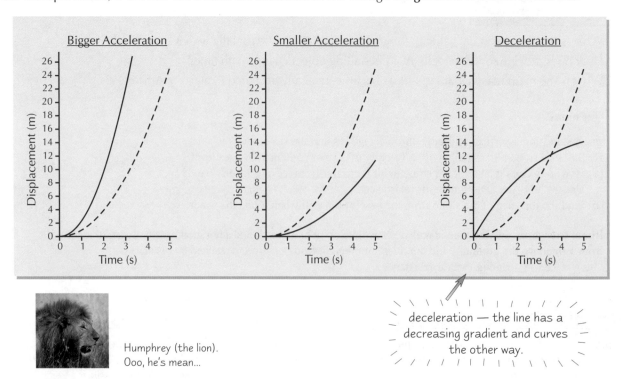

Humphrey (the lion).
Ooo, he's mean...

deceleration — the line has a decreasing gradient and curves the other way.

Displacement-Time Graphs

The **Gradient** of a **Displacement-Time Graph** Tells You the Velocity

When the velocity is constant, the graph's a **straight line**.
Velocity is defined as...

> velocity = $\dfrac{\text{change in displacement}}{\text{time taken}}$

On the graph, this is $\dfrac{\text{change in } y\ (\Delta y)}{\text{change in } x\ (\Delta x)}$, i.e. the gradient.

So to get the velocity from a displacement-time graph,
just find the gradient.

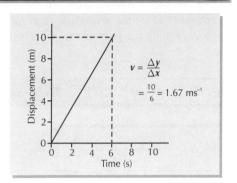

$v = \dfrac{\Delta y}{\Delta x}$
$= \dfrac{10}{6} = 1.67 \text{ ms}^{-1}$

It's the Same with **Curved Graphs**

If the gradient **isn't constant** (i.e. if it's a curved
line), it means the object is **accelerating**.

> To find the **velocity** at a certain point you
> need to draw a **tangent** to the curve at
> that point and find its gradient.

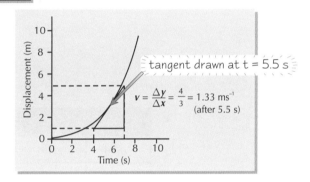

tangent drawn at t = 5.5 s

$v = \dfrac{\Delta y}{\Delta x} = \dfrac{4}{3} = 1.33 \text{ ms}^{-1}$
(after 5.5 s)

Practice Questions

Q1 What is given by the slope of a displacement-time graph?

Q2 Sketch a displacement-time graph to show: a) constant velocity, b) acceleration, c) deceleration

Exam Questions

Q1 Describe the motion of the cyclist as shown by the graph below. [4 marks]

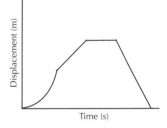

Q2 A baby crawls 5 m in 8 seconds at a constant velocity. She then rests for 5 seconds before crawling a further
3 m in 5 seconds. Finally, she makes her way back to her starting point in 10 seconds, travelling at a constant
speed all the way.
(a) Draw a displacement-time graph to show the baby's journey. [4 marks]
(b) Calculate her velocity at all the different stages of her journey. [2 marks]

Some curves are bigger than others...

Whether it's a straight line or a curve, the steeper it is, the greater the velocity. There's nothing difficult about these graphs — the main problem is that it's easy to get them muddled up with velocity-time graphs (next page). If in doubt, think about the gradient — is it velocity or acceleration, is it changing (curve), is it constant (straight line), is it 0 (horizontal line)...

Velocity-Time Graphs

These pages are for AQA A Unit 2, Edexcel Unit 1, OCR A Unit 1 and OCR B Unit 2.

Speed-time graphs and velocity-time graphs are pretty similar. The big difference is that velocity-time graphs can have a negative part to show something travelling in the opposite direction:

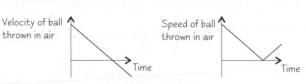

The **Gradient** of a **Velocity-Time Graph** tells you the **Acceleration**

$$acceleration = \frac{change\ in\ velocity}{time\ taken}$$

likewise for a speed-time graph

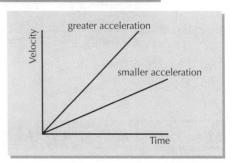

So the acceleration is just the **gradient** of a **velocity-time graph**.

1) **Uniform** acceleration is always a **straight line**.
2) The **steeper** the **gradient**, the **greater** the **acceleration**.

Example

A lion strolls along at 1.5 ms⁻¹ for 4 s and then accelerates uniformly at a rate of 2.5 ms⁻² for 4 s. Plot this information on a velocity-time graph.

So, for the first four seconds, the velocity is 1.5 ms⁻¹, then it increases by **2.5 ms⁻¹ every second**:

t (s)	v (ms⁻¹)
0 – 4	**1.5**
5	**4.0**
6	**6.5**
7	**9.0**
8	**11.5**

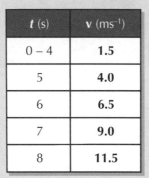

Percy (the lion)...

You can see that the **gradient of the line** is **constant** between 4 s and 8 s and has a value of 2.5 ms⁻², representing the **acceleration of the lion**.

Distance *Travelled* = **Area** under **Speed-Time Graph**

You know that:

distance travelled = average speed × time

So you can find the distance travelled by working out the **area under a speed-time graph**.

Example

A racing car accelerates uniformly from rest to 40 ms⁻¹ in 10 s. It maintains this speed for a further 20 s before coming to rest by decelerating at a constant rate over the next 15 s. Draw a velocity-time graph for this journey and use it to calculate the total distance travelled by the racing car.

Split the **graph** up into **sections**: A, B and C
Calculate the **area** of each and **add** the three results together.
A: Area = ½ base × height = ½ × 10 × 40 = 200 m
B: Area = b × h = 20 × 40 = 800 m
C: Area = ½ b × h = ½ × 15 × 40 = 300 m
Total distance travelled = 1300 m

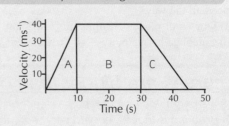

Velocity-Time Graphs

Non-Uniform Acceleration is a Curve on a V-T Graph

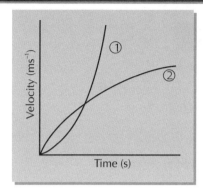

1) If the acceleration is changing, the gradient of the velocity-time graph will also be changing — so you **won't** get a **straight line**.

2) **Increasing acceleration** is shown by an **increasing gradient** — like in curve ①.

3) **Decreasing acceleration** is shown by a **decreasing gradient** — like in curve ②.

Simple enough...

You Can Draw Displacement-Time and Velocity-Time Graphs Using ICT

Instead of gathering distance and time data using **traditional methods**, e.g. a stopwatch and ruler, you can be a bit more **high-tech**.

A fairly **standard** piece of kit you can use for motion experiments is an **ultrasound position detector**. This is a type of **data-logger** that automatically records the **distance** of an object from the sensor several times a second.

If you attach one of these detectors to a computer with **graph-drawing software**, you can get **real-time** displacement-time and velocity-time graphs.

The main **advantages** of data-loggers over traditional methods are:

1) The data is more **accurate** — you don't have to allow for human reaction times.

2) Automatic systems have a much higher **sampling** rate than humans — most ultrasound position detectors can take a reading ten times every second.

3) You can see the data displayed in **real time**.

Practice Questions

Q1   How do you calculate acceleration from a velocity-time graph?

Q2   How do you calculate the distance travelled from a speed-time graph?

Q3   Sketch velocity-time graphs for constant velocity and constant acceleration.

Q4   Describe the main advantages of ICT over traditional methods for the collection and display of motion data.

Exam Question

Q1   A skier accelerates uniformly from rest at 2 ms^{-2} down a straight slope.

(a) Sketch a velocity-time graph for the first 5 s of his journey.   [2 marks]

(b) Use a constant acceleration equation to calculate his displacement at t = 1, 2, 3, 4 and 5 s, and plot this information onto a displacement-time graph.   [5 marks]

(c) Suggest another method of calculating the skier's distance travelled after each second and use this to check your answers to part (b).   [2 marks]

Still awake — I'll give you five more minutes...

There's a really nice sunset outside my window. It's one of those ones that makes the whole landscape go pinky-yellowish. And that's about as much interest as I can muster on this topic. Normal service will be resumed on page 17, I hope.

Mass, Weight and Centre of Gravity

These pages are for AQA A Unit 2, Edexcel Unit 1 and OCR A Unit 1.

I'm sure you know all this 'mass', 'weight' and 'density' stuff from GCSE. But let's just make sure...

The Mass of a Body makes it Resist Changes in Motion

1) The **mass** of an object is the **amount of 'stuff'** (or **matter**) in it. It's measured in **kg**.
2) The greater an object's mass, the greater its **resistance** to a **change in velocity** (called its **inertia**).
3) The **mass** of an object **doesn't change** if the strength of the **gravitational field** changes.
4) Weight is a **force**. It's measured in **newtons** (N), like all forces.
5) Weight is the **force experienced by a mass** due to a **gravitational field**.
6) The weight of an object **does vary** according to the size of the **gravitational field** acting on it.

weight = mass × gravitational field strength (W = mg)   where g = 9.81 Nkg⁻¹ on Earth.

This table shows Wilfred (the lion*)'s mass and weight on the Earth and the Moon.

Name	Quantity	Earth (g = 9.81 Nkg⁻¹)	Moon (g = 1.6 Nkg⁻¹)
Mass	Mass (scalar)	150 kg	150 kg
Weight	Force (vector)	1471.5 N	240 N

Weight 240 N

Weight 1470 N

Density is Mass per Unit Volume

Density is a measure of the 'compactness' (for want of a better word) of a substance.
It relates the mass of a substance to how much space it takes up.

$$density = \frac{mass}{volume} \qquad \rho = \frac{m}{V}$$

The symbol for density is a Greek letter rho (ρ) — it looks like a p but it isn't.

The **units** of **density** are **g cm⁻³** or **kg m⁻³**
N.B. 1 g cm⁻³ = 1000 kg m⁻³

1) The density of an object depends on what it's made of. Density **doesn't vary** with **size or shape**.
2) The **average density** of an object determines whether it **floats** or **sinks**.
3) A solid object will **float** on a fluid if it has a **lower density** than the **fluid**.

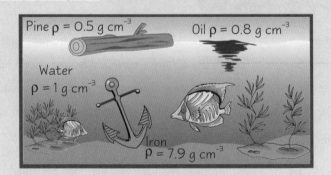
Pine ρ = 0.5 g cm⁻³ Oil ρ = 0.8 g cm⁻³ Water ρ = 1 g cm⁻³ Iron ρ = 7.9 g cm⁻³

Centre of Gravity — Assume All the Mass is in One Place

1) The **centre of gravity** (or centre of mass) of an object is the **single point** that you can consider its **whole weight** to **act through** (whatever its orientation).
2) The object will always **balance** around this **point**, although in some cases the **centre of gravity** will **fall outside** the object.

Centre of gravity

Centre of gravity

Centre of gravity

*Yes, I know — I just like lions, OK...

Mass, Weight and Centre of Gravity

Find the Centre of Gravity either by Symmetry or Experiment

Experiment to find the Centre of Gravity of an Irregular Object

1) Hang the object freely from a point (e.g. one corner).
2) Draw a vertical line downwards from the point of suspension — use a plumb bob to get your line exactly vertical.
3) Hang the object from a different point.
4) Draw another vertical line down.
5) The centre of gravity is where the two lines cross.

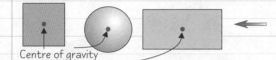

For a regular object you can just use symmetry. The centre of gravity of any regular shape is at its centre.

Centre of gravity

How High the Centre of Gravity is tells you How Stable the Object is

1) An object will be nice and **stable** if it has a **low centre** of **gravity** and a **wide base area**. This idea is used a lot in design, e.g. Formula 1 racing cars.

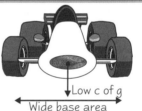

Low c of g
Wide base area

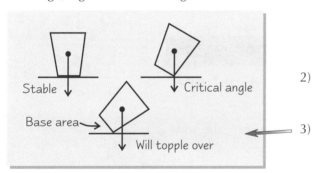

Stable

Critical angle

Base area

Will topple over

2) The **higher** the **centre of gravity**, and the **smaller** the **base area**, the **less stable** the object will be. Think of unicyclists...

3) An object will topple over if a **vertical line** drawn **downwards** from its **centre of gravity** falls **outside** its **base area**.

Practice Questions

Q1 A lioness has a mass of 200 kg. What would be her mass and weight on the Earth (where g = 9.8 Nkg⁻¹) and on the Moon (where g = 1.6 Nkg⁻¹)?

Q2 What is meant by the centre of gravity of an object?

Exam Questions

Q1 (a) Define **density**. [1 mark]

(b) A cylinder of aluminium, radius 4 cm and height 6 cm, has a mass of 820 g. Calculate its density. [3 marks]

(c) Use the information from part (b) to calculate the mass of a cube of aluminium of side 5 cm. [1 mark]

Q2 Describe an experiment to find the centre of gravity of an object of uniform density with a constant thickness and irregular cross-section. Identify one major source of uncertainty and suggest a way to reduce its effect on the accuracy of your result. [5 marks]

The centre of gravity of this book should be round about page 64...

This is a really useful area of physics. To would-be nuclear physicists it might seem a little dull, but if you want to be an engineer — something a bit more useful (no offence Einstein) — then things like centre of gravity and density are dead important things to understand. You know, for designing things like cars and submarines... yep, pretty useful I'd say.

Forces

These pages are for AQA A Unit 2, Edexcel Unit 1, OCR A Unit 1 and OCR B Unit 2.

Remember the vector stuff from the beginning of the section... good, you're going to need it...

Free-Body Force Diagrams *show* All Forces *on a* Single Body

1) **Free-body force** diagrams show a **single body** on its own.

2) The diagram should include all the **forces** that **act on** the body, but **not** the **forces it exerts** on the rest of the world.

3) Remember **forces** are **vector quantities** and so the **arrow labels** should show the **size** and **direction** of the forces.

4) If a body is in **equilibrium** (i.e. not accelerating) the **forces** acting on it will be **balanced**.

Drawing free-body force diagrams isn't too hard — you just need practice. Here are a few **examples**:

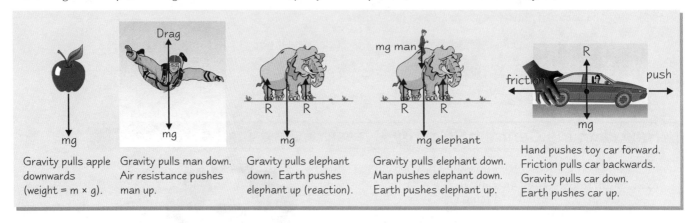

Gravity pulls apple downwards (weight = m × g).	Gravity pulls man down. Air resistance pushes man up.	Gravity pulls elephant down. Earth pushes elephant up (reaction).	Gravity pulls elephant down. Man pushes elephant down. Earth pushes elephant up.	Hand pushes toy car forward. Friction pulls car backwards. Gravity pulls car down. Earth pushes car up.

Resolving *a* Force *means* Splitting *it into* Components

1) Forces can be in **any direction**, so they're not always at right angles to each other. This is sometimes a bit **awkward** for **calculations**.

2) To make an 'awkward' force easier to deal with, you can think of it as **two separate forces**, acting at **right angles to each other**.

The force **F** has exactly the same effect as the horizontal and vertical forces, F_H and F_V.

Replacing **F** with F_H and F_V is called **resolving the force F**.

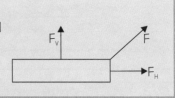

3) To find the size of a component force in a particular direction, you need to use trigonometry (see page 5). Forces are vectors, so you treat them in the same way as velocities — put them end to end.

So this...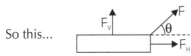

...could be drawn like this:

Using trig. you get:

$$\frac{F_H}{F} = \cos\theta \quad \textbf{or} \quad F_H = F\cos\theta$$

And:

$$\frac{F_V}{F} = \sin\theta \quad \textbf{or} \quad F_V = F\sin\theta$$

Example

A tree trunk is pulled along the ground by an elephant exerting a force of 1200 N at an angle of 25° to the horizontal. Calculate the components of this force in the horizontal and vertical directions.

Horizontal force = 1200 × cos 25° = **1088 N**

Vertical force = 1200 × sin 25° = **507 N**

Forces

You Add the Components Back Together to get the Resultant Force

1) If **two forces** act on an object, you find the **resultant** (total) **force** by adding the **vectors** together and creating a **closed triangle**, with the resultant force represented by the **third side**.

2) Forces are vectors (as you know), so you use **vector addition** — draw the forces as vector arrows put 'tail to top'.

3) Then it's yet more trigonometry to find the **angle** and the **length** of the third side.

Example

Two dung beetles roll a dung ball along the ground at constant velocity. Beetle A applies a force of 0.5 N northwards while beetle B exerts a force of only 0.2 N eastwards. What is the resultant force on the dung ball?

The resultant force is **0.54 N** at an angle of **21.8°** from North.

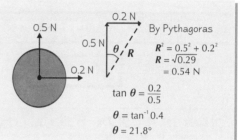

By Pythagoras
$R^2 = 0.5^2 + 0.2^2$
$R = \sqrt{0.29}$
$= 0.54$ N

$\tan \theta = \frac{0.2}{0.5}$

$\theta = \tan^{-1} 0.4$
$\theta = 21.8°$

Choose sensible Axes for Resolving

Use directions that **make sense** for the situation you're dealing with. If you've got an object on a slope, choose your directions **along the slope** and **at right angles to it**. You can turn the paper to an angle if that helps.

Always choose sensible axes

Examiners like to call a slope an "inclined plane".

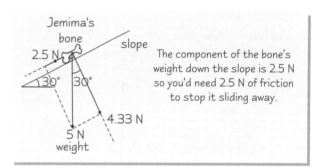

The component of the bone's weight down the slope is 2.5 N so you'd need 2.5 N of friction to stop it sliding away.

Practice Questions

Q1 Sketch a free-body force diagram for an ice hockey puck moving across the ice (assuming no friction).

Q2 What are the horizontal and vertical components of the force F?

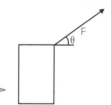

Exam Questions

Q1 A picture is suspended from a hook as shown in the diagram. Calculate the tension force, T, in the string.

[2 marks]

Q2 Two elephants pull a tree trunk as shown in the diagram. Calculate the resultant force on the tree trunk.

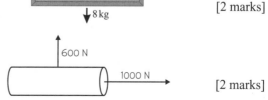

[2 marks]

Free-body force diagram — sounds like something you'd get with a dance mat...

*Remember those F cos θ and F sin θ bits. Write them on bits of paper and stick them to your wall. Scrawl them on your pillow. Tattoo them on your brain. Whatever it takes — you just **have to learn them**.*

Moments and Torques

These pages are for *AQA A Unit 2* and *OCR A Unit 1*.

This is not a time for jokes. There is not a moment to lose. The time for torquing is over. Oh ho ho ho ho *bang*. (Ow.)

A **Moment** is the **Turning Effect** of a **Force**

The **moment**, or **torque**, of a **force** depends on the **size** of the force and **how far** the force is applied from the **turning point**:

> **moment of a force** (in Nm) = **force** (in N) × **perpendicular distance from pivot** (in m)

In symbols, that's: $$M = F \times d$$

Moments must be **Balanced** or the **Object** will **Turn**

The **principle of moments** states that for a body to be in **equilibrium**, the **sum of the clockwise moments** about any point **equals** the **sum of the anticlockwise moments** about the same point.

Example

Two children sit on a seesaw as shown in the diagram. An adult balances the seesaw at one end. Find the size and direction of the force that the adult needs to apply.

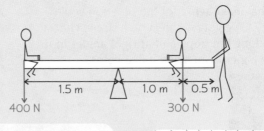

1.5 m   1.0 m   0.5 m
400 N   300 N

In equilibrium, $\sum$ anticlockwise moments = $\sum$ clockwise moments

$$400 \times 1.5 = 300 \times 1 + 1.5F$$
$$600 = 300 + 1.5F$$

Final answer: F = 200 N downwards

> $\sum$ means "the sum of"

Muscles, **Bones** and **Joints** Act as **Levers**

1) In a lever, an **effort force** (in this case from a muscle) acts against a **load force** (e.g. the weight of your arm) by means of a **rigid object** (the bone) rotating around a **pivot** (the joint).

2) You can use the **principle of moments** to answer lever questions:

Example

Find the force exerted by the biceps in holding a bag of gold still. The bag of gold weighs 100 N and the forearm weighs 20 N.

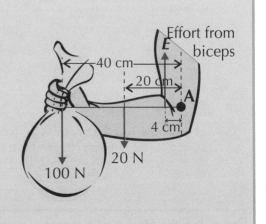

Effort from
E
biceps
40 cm
20 cm
A
4 cm
20 N
100 N

Take moments about **A**.

In equilibrium:

$\sum$ anticlockwise moments = $\sum$ clockwise moments

$$(100 \times 0.4) + (20 \times 0.2) = 0.04E$$
$$40 + 4 = 0.04E$$

Final answer: E = 1100 N

Moments and Torques

A **Couple** is a **Pair** of **Forces**

1) A couple is a **pair** of **forces** of **equal size** which act
    parallel to each other, but in **opposite directions**.

2) A couple doesn't cause any resultant linear force, but **does** produce
    a **turning force** (usually called a **torque** rather than a moment).

The **size** of this **torque** depends on the **size** of the **forces** and the
distance between them.

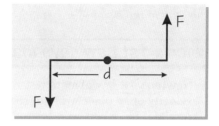

> **Torque of a couple** (in Nm) = **size of one of the forces** (in N) × **perpendicular distance between the forces** (in m)

In symbols, that's: $T = F \times d$

Example

A cyclist turns a sharp right corner by applying equal but
opposite forces of 20 N to the ends of the handlebars.

The length of the handlebars is 0.6 m.
Calculate the torque applied to the handlebars.

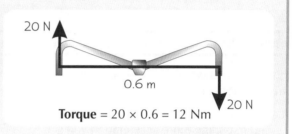

Torque = 20 × 0.6 = 12 Nm

Practice Questions

Q1   A girl of mass 40 kg sits 1.5 m from the middle of a seesaw.
     Show that her brother, mass 50 kg, must sit 1.2 m from the middle if the seesaw is to balance.

Q2   What is meant by the word 'couple'?

Exam Questions

Q1   A driver is changing his flat tyre. The torque required to undo the nut is 60 Nm.
     He uses a 0.4 m long double-ended wheel wrench.
     Calculate the force that he must apply at each end of the spanner.   [2 marks]

Q2   A diver of mass 60 kg stands on the end of a diving board 2 m from the pivot point.
     Calculate the upward force exerted on the retaining spring 30 cm from the pivot.

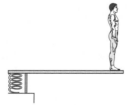

[2 marks]

It's all about balancing — just ask a tightrope walker...

*They're always seesaw questions aren't they. It'd be nice if once, **just once**, they'd have a question on... I don't know,
rotating knives or something. Just something unexpected... anything. It'd make physics a lot more fun, I'm sure. *sigh**

Newton's Laws of Motion

Page 22 is for AQA A Unit 2, Edexcel Unit 1, OCR A Unit 1 and OCR B Unit 2. 3rd law is for AQA A and Edexcel only.

You did most of this at GCSE, but that doesn't mean you can just skip over it now. You'll be kicking yourself if you forget this stuff in the exam — easy marks...

Newton's **1st Law** says that a **Force** is Needed to Change Velocity

1) **Newton's 1st law of motion** states that the **velocity** of an object will **not change** unless a **resultant force** acts on it.

2) In plain English this means a body will stay still or move in a **straight line** at a **constant speed**, unless there's a **resultant force** acting on it.

3) If the forces **aren't balanced**, the **overall resultant force** will make the body **accelerate**. This could be a change in **direction**, or **speed**, or both. (See Newton's 2nd law, below.)

An apple sitting on a table won't go anywhere because the **forces** on it are **balanced**.

reaction (R)	=	**weight** (mg)
(force of table pushing apple up)		(force of gravity pulling apple down)

Newton's **2nd Law** says that **Acceleration** is **Proportional** to the Force

...which can be written as the well-known equation:

resultant force (N) = mass (kg) × acceleration (ms⁻²)

$$F = m \times a$$

Learn this — it crops up all over the place in AS Physics. And learn what it means too:

1) It says that the **more force** you have acting on a certain mass, the **more acceleration** you get.

2) It says that for a given force the **more mass** you have, the **less acceleration** you get.

REMEMBER:
1) The **resultant force** is the **vector sum** of all the forces.
2) The force is **always** measured in **newtons**.
3) The **mass** is always measured in **kilograms**.
4) The **acceleration** is always in the **same direction** as the **resultant force** and is measured in ms⁻².

Galileo said: **All Objects Fall** at the **Same Rate** (if you **Ignore Air Resistance**)

You need to understand **why** this is true. Newton's 2nd law explains it neatly — consider two balls dropped at the same time — ball **1** being heavy, and ball **2** being light. Then use Newton's 2nd law to find their acceleration.

mass = m_1
resultant force = F_1
acceleration = a_1
By Newton's Second Law:
$$F_1 = m_1 a_1$$
Ignoring air resistance, the only force acting on the ball is weight, given by $W_1 = m_1 g$ (where g = gravitational field strength = 9.81 Nkg⁻¹).
So: $F_1 = m_1 a_1 = W_1 = m_1 g$
So: $m_1 a_1 = m_1 g$, then m_1 cancels out to give: $a_1 = g$

mass = m_2
resultant force = F_2
acceleration = a_2
By Newton's Second Law:
$$F_2 = m_2 a_2$$
Ignoring air resistance, the only force acting on the ball is weight, given by $W_2 = m_2 g$ (where g = gravitational field strength = 9.81 Nkg⁻¹).
So: $F_2 = m_2 a_2 = W_2 = m_2 g$
So: $m_2 a_2 = m_2 g$, then m_2 cancels out to give: $a_2 = g$

... in other words, the **acceleration** is **independent of the mass**. It makes **no difference** whether the ball is **heavy or light**. And I've kindly **hammered home the point** by showing you two almost identical examples.

Newton's Laws Are Only **Approximations**

OCR A only

Newton's laws work pretty well. At **everyday speeds** they give really, really good approximations — but they're **not** the whole story. At very **high speeds**, you have to take into account **relativistic effects**. According to the **Special Theory of Relativity**, as you increase the speed of an object its **mass increases**. So mass isn't constant, and $F = ma$ doesn't work any more.

Newton's Laws of Motion

Newton's **3rd Law** says each Force has an **Equal**, Opposite Reaction Force

There are a few different ways of stating Newton's 3rd law, but the clearest way is:

> **If an object A EXERTS a FORCE on object B, then object B exerts AN EQUAL BUT OPPOSITE FORCE on object A.**

You'll also hear the law as "every action has an equal and opposite reaction". But this confuses people who wrongly think the forces are both applied to the same object. (If that were the case, you'd get a resultant force of zero and nothing would ever move anywhere...)

The two forces actually represent the **same interaction**, just seen from two **different perspectives**:

1) If you **push against a wall**, the wall will **push back** against you, **just as hard**. As soon as you stop pushing, so does the wall. Amazing...

2) If you **pull a cart**, whatever force **you exert** on the rope, the rope exerts the **exact opposite** pull on you (unless the rope's stretching).

3) When you go **swimming**, you push **back** against the water with your arms and legs, and the water pushes you **forwards** with an equal-sized force.

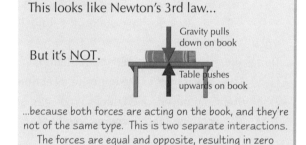

This looks like Newton's 3rd law...

But it's <u>NOT</u>.

Gravity pulls down on book

Table pushes upwards on book

...because both forces are acting on the book, and they're not of the same type. This is two separate interactions. The forces are equal and opposite, resulting in zero acceleration, so this is showing Newton's 1st law.

Newton's 3rd law applies in **all situations** and to all **types of force**. But the pairs of forces are always the **same type**, e.g. both gravitational or both electrical.

Practice Questions

Q1 State Newton's 1st, 2nd and 3rd laws of motion, and explain what they mean.

Q2 What are the two equal and opposite forces acting between an orbiting satellite and the Earth?

Exam Questions

Q1 Draw diagrams to show the forces acting on a parachutist:
   (a) accelerating downwards. [1 mark]
   (b) having reached terminal velocity. [1 mark]

Q2 A boat is moving across a river. The engines provide a force of 500 N at right angles to the flow of the river and the boat experiences a drag of 100 N in the opposite direction. The force on the boat due to the flow of the river is 300 N. The mass of the boat is 250 kg.
   (a) Calculate the magnitude of the resultant force acting on the boat. [2 marks]
   (b) Calculate the magnitude of the acceleration of the boat. [2 marks]

Q3 This question asks you to use Newton's second law to explain three situations.
   (a) Two cars have different maximum accelerations.
       What are the only two overall factors that determine the acceleration a car can have? [2 marks]
   (b) Michael can always beat his younger brother Tom in a sprint, however short the distance.
       Give two possible reasons for this. [2 marks]
   (c) Michael and Tom are both keen on diving. They notice that they seem to take the same time to drop
       from the diving board to the water. Explain why this is the case. (Assume no air resistance.) [3 marks]

<u>Newton's three incredibly important laws of motion...</u>

These laws may not really fill you with a huge amount of excitement (and I could hardly blame you if they don't)... but it was pretty fantastic at the time — suddenly people actually understood how forces work, and how they affect motion. I mean arguably it was one of the most important scientific discoveries ever...

Terminal Velocity

These pages are for AQA A Unit 2 and OCR A Unit 1.

If you jump out of a plane at 2000 ft, you want to know that you're not going to be accelerating all the way.

Friction is a Force that Opposes Motion

There are two main types of friction:

1) **Contact friction** between **solid surfaces** (which is what we usually mean when we just use the word 'friction'). You don't need to worry about that too much for now.

2) **Fluid friction** (known as **drag** or fluid resistance or air resistance).

> **Fluid Friction or Drag:**
> 1) 'Fluid' is a word that means either a **liquid or a gas** — something that can **flow**.
> 2) The force depends on the thickness (or **viscosity**) of the fluid.
> 3) It **increases** as the **speed increases** (for simple situations it's directly proportional, but you don't need to worry about the mathematical relationship).
> 4) It also depends on the **shape** of the object moving through it — the larger the **area** pushing against the fluid, the greater the resistance force.

Things you need to remember about frictional forces:

1) They **always** act in the **opposite direction** to the **motion** of the object.

2) They can **never** speed things up or start something moving.

3) They convert **kinetic energy** into **heat**.

Terminal Velocity — when the Friction Force Equals the Driving Force

You will reach a **terminal velocity** at some point, if you have:

    1) a **driving force** that stays the **same** all the time

    2) a **frictional** or **drag force** (or collection of forces) that increases with speed

There are **three main stages** to reaching terminal velocity:

The car **accelerates** from **rest** using a constant driving force.

As the **velocity increases**, the **resistance forces increase** (because of things like turbulence — you don't need the details). This **reduces the resultant force** on the car and hence **reduces its acceleration**.

Eventually the car reaches a velocity at which the **resistance forces are equal to the driving force**. There is now **no resultant force** and **no acceleration**, so the car carries on at **constant velocity**.

Sketching a Graph for Terminal Velocity

You need to be able to **recognise** and **sketch** the graphs for **velocity against time** and **acceleration against time** for the **terminal velocity** situation.

Nothing for it but practice — shut the book and sketch them from memory. Keep doing it till you get them right every time.

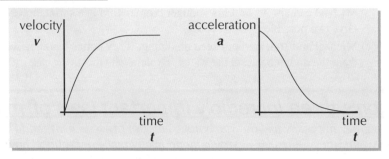

Terminal Velocity

*Things **Falling** through **Air** or **Water** Reach a **Terminal Velocity** too*

When something's falling through **air**, the **weight** of the object is a **constant force** accelerating the object downwards. **Air resistance** is a **frictional force** opposing this motion, which **increases** with **speed**.
So before a parachutist opens the parachute, exactly the same thing happens as with the car example:

1) A skydiver leaves a plane and will **accelerate** until the **air resistance** equals his **weight**.

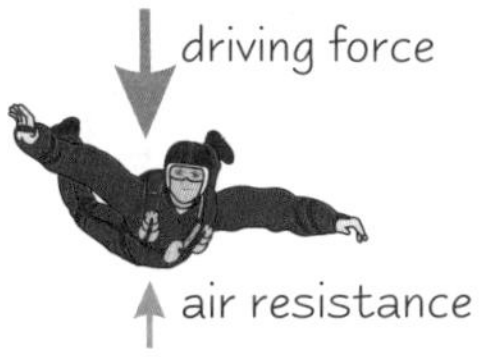

2) He will then be travelling at a **terminal velocity**.

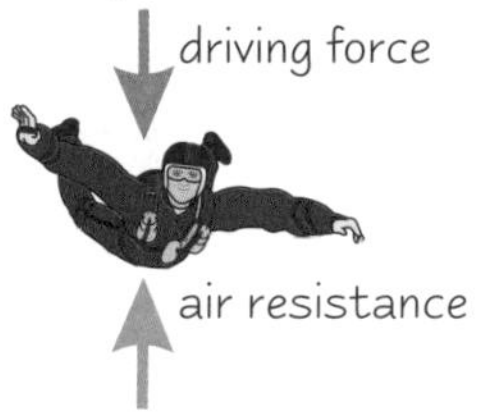

But... the terminal velocity of a person in free fall is too great to land without dying a horrible death.
The **parachute increases** the **air resistance massively**, which slows him down to a lower terminal velocity:

3) Before reaching the ground he will **open his parachute**, which immediately **increases the air resistance** so it is now **bigger** than his **weight**.

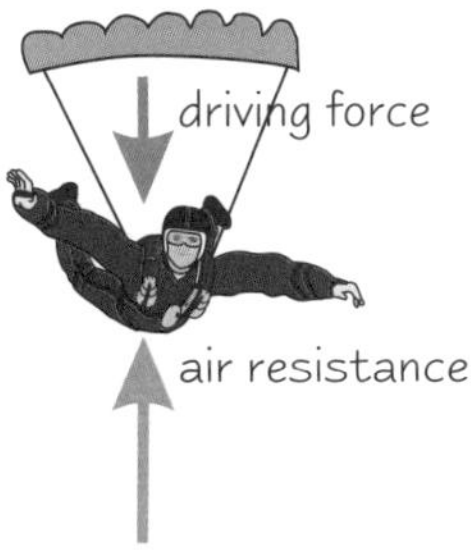

4) This **slows him down** until his speed has dropped enough for the **air resistance** to be **equal to his weight** again. This new terminal velocity is small enough to survive landing.

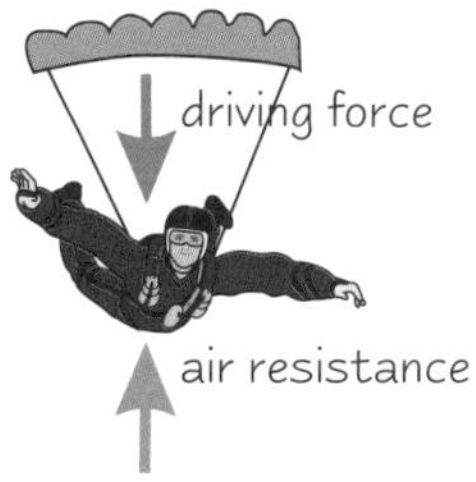

The v-t graph is a bit different, because you have a new terminal velocity being reached after the parachute is opened:

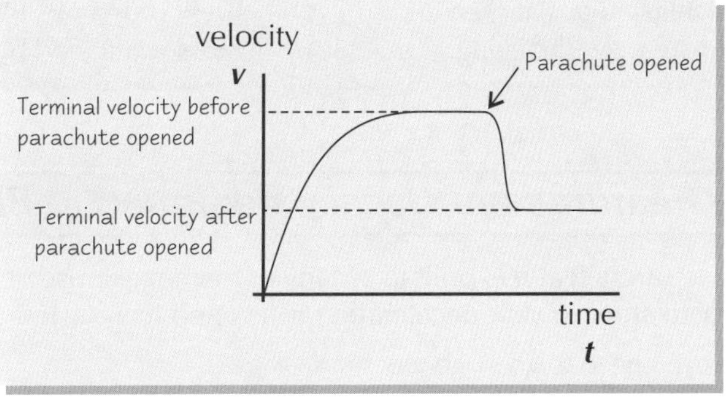

Practice Questions

Q1 What forces limit the speed of a skier going down a slope?

Q2 What conditions cause a terminal velocity to be reached?

Q3 Sketch a graph to show how the velocity changes with time for an object falling through air.

Exam Question

Q1 A space probe free-falls towards the surface of a planet.
The graph on the right shows the velocity data recorded by the probe as it falls.

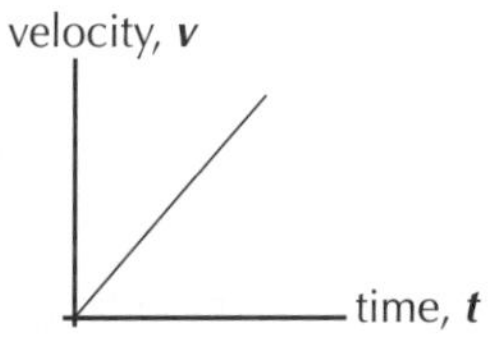

(a) The planet does not have an atmosphere. Explain how you can tell this from the graph. [2 marks]

(b) Sketch the velocity-time graph you would expect to see if the planet did have an atmosphere. [2 marks]

(c) Explain the shape of the graph you have drawn. [3 marks]

You'll never understand this without going parachuting...*

When you're doing questions about terminal velocity, remember the frictional forces reduce acceleration, not speed. They usually don't slow an object down, apart from in the parachute example, where the skydiver is travelling faster when the parachute opens than the terminal velocity for the parachute-skydiver combination.

* No. 37 in a series of the 100 least convincing excuses for an interesting holiday.

Forces on Vehicles and Car Safety

These pages are for OCR A Unit 1. Page 26 is also worth a look for Edexcel Unit 1 as an 'application of mechanics'.

Some real applications now — how to avoid collisions, and how car manufacturers try to make sure you survive.

Many Factors Affect How Quickly a Car Stops

The braking distance and thinking distance together make the **total distance you need to stop** after you see a problem:

Thinking distance + Braking distance = Stopping distance

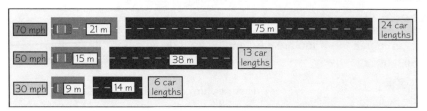 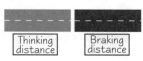

In an exam you might need to list factors that affect the thinking and braking distances.

> **thinking distance = speed × reaction time**
> **Reaction time** is increased by **tiredness, alcohol** or other **drug** use, **illness, distractions** such as noisy children and Wayne's World-style headbanging.

> **Braking distance** depends on the **braking force, friction** between the tyres and the road, the **mass** and the **speed**.
> **Braking force** is reduced by **reduced friction** between the brakes and the wheels (**worn** or **badly adjusted brakes**).
> **Friction** between the tyres and the road is reduced by **wet** or **icy** roads, **leaves or dirt** on the road, **worn-out tyre treads**, etc.
> **Mass** is affected by the size of the car and what you put in it.

Car Safety Features are Usually Designed to Slow You Down Gradually

Modern cars have **safety features** built in. Many of them make use of the idea of slowing the collision down so it **takes you longer to stop**, so your **deceleration is less** and there is **less force** on you.

Safety features you need to know about are:

1) **Seatbelts** keep you in your seat and also 'give' a little so that you're brought to a stop over a longer time.

2) **Airbags** inflate when you have a collision and are big and squishy so they stop you hitting hard things and slow you down gradually. (More about airbags and how they work on the next page.)

3) **Crumple zones** at the front and back of the car are designed to give way more easily and absorb some of the energy of the collision.

4) **Safety cages** are designed to prevent the area around the occupants of the car from being crushed in.

> ### Example
> Giles's car bumps into the back of a stationary bus. The car was travelling at 2 ms⁻¹ and comes to a stop in 0.2 s. Giles was wearing his seatbelt and takes 0.8 s to stop. The mass of the car is 1000 kg and Giles's mass is 75 kg.
> a) Find the decelerations of Giles and the car.
> b) Calculate the average force acting on Giles during the accident.
> c) Work out the average force that would have acted on Giles if he had stopped in as short a time as the car.
>
> a) Use $v = u + at$:
> For the car: $u = 2$ ms⁻¹, $v = 0$, $t = 0.2$ s
> Which gives: $0 = 2 + 0.2a \Rightarrow 0.2a = -2 \Rightarrow a = -10$ ms⁻² so the **deceleration = 10 ms⁻²**
> For Giles: $u = 2$ ms⁻¹, $v = 0$, $t = 0.8$ s
> Which gives: $0 = 2 + 0.8a \Rightarrow 0.8a = -2 \Rightarrow a = -2.5$ ms⁻² so the **deceleration = 2.5 ms⁻²**
> b) Use $F = ma = 75 \times 2.5 =$ **187.5 N**
> c) Use $F = ma$ again, but with 10 ms⁻² instead of 2.5 ms⁻²: $F = ma = 75 \times 10 =$ **750 N**

Forces on Vehicles and Car Safety

Airbags are Triggered by Rapid Deceleration

It's pretty hard going trying to get an airbag to go off when you need it — and not end up having a face full of airbag every time you stop at traffic lights. Here's how they work...

1) All airbags are **triggered to inflate using** sensors that detect the **rapid deceleration** of a car in a crash.

2) Most cars use a microchip **accelerometer** — where **rapid deceleration** changes the **capacitance** of part of the microchip. This change can be detected by the microchip's electronics, which send an "inflate now" signal to the airbag modules in the car.

3) This kicks off a rapid **chemical reaction** that produces a load of inert gas to inflate the air bag.

4) It's a lot to do in a very **short space of time** if it's going to get to your head before you get up close and personal with a steering wheel. Airbags inflate in less than a tenth of a second once triggered.

5) As soon as they're inflated, the airbags begin to deflate as gas escapes through flaps in the fabric.

GPS Devices Find Where You Are Using Trilateration

Some cars are fitted with glitzy global positioning systems (**GPS**) to help you find out **where** you are. They do this using a process called **trilateration**...

1) The GPS in your car receives signals from at least **three satellites**, each transmitting their **location** and the **time** the signal was sent.

2) As the signals take a short amount of time to reach the GPS, there is a short **delay** between the time sent and the time each signal is received. The further away the satellite, the longer it takes the signal to get to your car.

3) By knowing the **time delay** for each satellite signal, the GPS can calculate the **distance** to each satellite. You then know that you must be somewhere on the surface of a sphere that's centred on that satellite.

4) If you know the distances to **three** satellites, you must be at the point where all three spheres **meet**. Clever, huh?

5) GPS systems actually use at least **four** satellites to locate you. You only need three, but the more satellites the more **accurately** you can know your position.

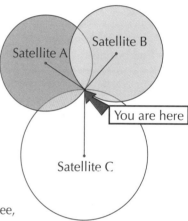

Practice Questions

Q1 What equation can you use to work out the force you experience during a collision?
Q2 What factor affects both thinking distance and braking distance?
Q3 Describe how airbags are triggered to inflate when a car is in a collision.

Exam Questions

Q1 Sarah sees a cow step into the road 30 m ahead of her. Sarah's reaction time is 0.5 s. She is travelling at 20 ms⁻¹. Her maximum braking force is 10 000 N and her car (with her in it) has a mass of 850 kg.
(a) How far does she travel before applying her brakes? [2 marks]
(b) Calculate Sarah's braking distance. Assume she applies the maximum braking force until she stops. [3 marks]
(c) Does Sarah hit the cow? Justify your answer with a suitable calculation. [1 mark]

Q2 In a crash test a car slams into a solid barrier at 20 ms⁻¹. The car comes to a halt in 0.1 s. The crash test dummy goes through the windscreen and hits the barrier at a speed of 18 ms⁻¹ and then also comes to a stop in 0.1 s. The mass of the car is 900 kg and the mass of the dummy is 50 kg.
(a) Calculate the forces on the car and the dummy as they are brought to a stop. [4 marks]
(b) The car is modified to include crumple zones and an airbag. Explain what difference this will make and why. [3 marks]

Crumple zone — the heap of clothes on my bedroom floor...

Being safe in a car is mainly common sense — don't drive if you're ill, drunk or just tired and don't drive a car with dodgy brakes. But you still need to cope with exam questions, so don't go on till you're sure you know this all off by heart.

Work and Power

These pages are for AQA A Unit 2, Edexcel Unit 1, OCR A Unit 1 and OCR B Unit 2.

As everyone knows, work in Physics isn't like normal work. It's harder. Work also has a specific meaning that's to do with movement and forces. You'll have seen this at GCSE — it just comes up in more detail for AS level.

Work is Done Whenever Energy is Transferred

This table gives you some examples of **work being done** and the **energy changes** that happen.

1) Usually you need a force to move something because you're having to **overcome another force**.

2) The thing being moved has **kinetic energy** while it's **moving**.

3) The kinetic energy is transferred to **another form of energy** when the movement stops.

ACTIVITY	WORK DONE AGAINST	FINAL ENERGY FORM
Lifting up a box.	gravity	gravitational potential energy
Pushing a chair across a level floor.	friction	heat
Pushing two magnetic north poles together.	magnetic force	magnetic energy
Stretching a spring.	stiffness of spring	elastic potential energy

The word **'work'** in Physics means the **amount of energy transferred** from one form to another when a force causes a movement of some sort.

Work = Force × Distance

When a car tows a caravan, it applies a force to the caravan to move it to where it's wanted. To **find out** how much **work** has been **done**, you need to use the **equation**:

> **work done (W) = force causing motion (F) × distance moved (s)**
> ...where **W** is measured in joules (J), **F** is measured in newtons (N) and **s** is measured in metres (m).

Points to remember:

1) **Work** is the **energy** that's been **changed** from one form to another — it's not necessarily the **total** energy. E.g. moving a book from a low shelf to a higher one will increase its gravitational potential energy, but it had some potential energy to start with. Here, the **work done** would be the **increase** in potential energy, **not the total** potential energy.

2) Remember the distance needs to be measured in metres — if you have **distance in centimetres or kilometres**, you need to **convert** it to metres first.

3) The force **F** will be a **fixed** value in any calculations, either because it's **constant** or because it's the **average** force.

4) The equation assumes that the **direction of the force** is the **same** as the **direction of movement**.

5) The equation gives you the **definition** of the joule (symbol J):
'One joule is the work done when a force of 1 newton moves an object through a distance of 1 metre'.

The Force isn't always in the Same Direction as the Movement

Sometimes the **direction of movement** is **different** from the **direction of the force**.

Example

1) To **calculate the work done** in a situation like the one on the right, you need to consider the **horizontal** and **vertical components** of the **force**.

2) The only **movement** is in the **horizontal** direction. This means the **vertical force** is not causing any motion (and hence not doing any work) — it's just **balancing** out some of the **weight**, meaning there's a **smaller reaction force**.

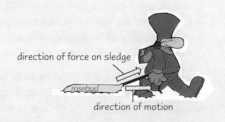

direction of force on sledge

rosebud

direction of motion

3) The horizontal force is causing the motion — so to **calculate** the **work done**, this is the **only force** you need to consider. Which means we get:

$$W = Fs \cos\theta$$

Where θ is the **angle** between the **direction of the force** and the **direction of motion**. See page 18 for more on resolving forces.

Work and Power

Power = Work Done per Second

Power means many things in everyday speech, but in physics (of course!) it has a special meaning. Power is the **rate of doing work** — in other words it is the **amount of energy transformed** from one form to another **per second.**
You **calculate power** from this equation:

> **Power (P) = work done (W) / time (t)**
> ...where **P** is measured in watts (W), **W** is measured in joules (J) and **t** is measured in seconds (s)

The **watt** (symbol W) is defined as a **rate of energy transfer** equal to **1 joule per second** (Js^{-1}).
Yep, that's another **equation and definition** for you to **learn**.

Power is also Force × Velocity (P = Fv)

Sometimes, it's **easier** to use **this version** of the power equation. This is how you get it:

1)   You **know** $P = W/t$.
2)   You also **know** $W = Fs$, which gives $P = Fs/t$.
3)   But $v = s/t$, which you can substitute into the above equation to give $P = Fv$.
4)   It's easier to use this if you're given the **speed** in the question.
     Learn this equation as a **shortcut** to link **power** and **speed**.

Example

A car is travelling at a speed of 10 ms^{-1} and is kept going against the frictional force by a driving force of 500 N in the direction of motion. Find the power supplied by the engine to keep the car moving.

Use the shortcut $P = Fv$, which gives:
$P = 500 \times 10 = 5000$ W

If the force and motion are in different directions, you can replace **F** with **F** cos θ to get: $\boxed{P = Fv\cos\theta}$

You **aren't** expected to **remember** this equation, but it's made up of bits that you **are supposed to know**, so be ready for the possibility of calculating **power** in a situation where the **direction of the force and direction of motion are different**.

Practice Questions

Q1   Write down the equation used to calculate work if the force and motion are in the same direction.

Q2   Write down the equation for work if the force is at an angle to the direction of motion.

Q3   Write down the equations relating (i) power and work and (ii) power and speed.

Exam Questions

Q1   A traditional narrowboat is drawn by a horse walking along the towpath.
The horse pulls the boat at a constant speed between two locks which are
1500 m apart. The tension in the rope is 100 N at 40° to the direction of motion.

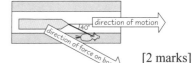

(a) How much work is done on the boat?   [2 marks]
(b) The boat moves at 0.8 ms^{-1}. Calculate the power supplied to the boat in the direction of motion.   [2 marks]

Q2   A motor is used to lift a 20 kg load a height of 3 m. (Take g = 9.81 Nkg^{-1}.)

(a) Calculate the work done in lifting the load.   [2 marks]
(b) The speed of the load during the lift is 0.25 ms^{-1}. Calculate the power delivered by the motor.   [2 marks]

Work — there's just no getting away from it...

Loads of equations to learn. Well, that's what you came here for, after all. Can't beat a good bit of equation-learning, as I've heard you say quietly to yourself when you think no one's listening. Aha, can't fool me. Ahahahahahahahahahahahahaha.

Conservation of Energy

These pages are for AQA A Unit 2, Edexcel Unit 1, OCR A Unit 1 and OCR B Unit 2.

Energy can never be *lost*. I repeat — *energy* can *never* be lost. Which is basically what I'm about to take up two whole pages saying. But that's, of course, because you need to do exam questions on this as well as understand the principle.

Learn the **Principle** of **Conservation** of **Energy**

The **principle of conservation of energy** says that:

Energy **cannot be created** or **destroyed**. Energy **can be transferred** from one form to another but the total amount of energy in a closed system will not change.

Example

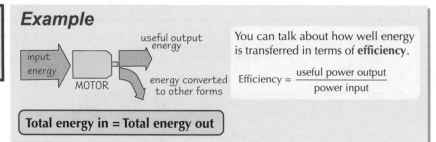

You can talk about how well energy is transferred in terms of **efficiency**.

$$\text{Efficiency} = \frac{\text{useful power output}}{\text{power input}}$$

Total energy in = Total energy out

You need it for **Questions** about **Kinetic** and **Potential Energy**

The principle of conservation of energy nearly always comes up when you're doing questions about changes between kinetic and potential energy.

A quick reminder:

1) **Kinetic energy** is energy of anything **moving**, which you work out from $E_k = \frac{1}{2}mv^2$, where v is the velocity it's travelling at and m is its mass.

2) There are **different types of potential energy** — e.g. gravitational and elastic.

3) **Gravitational potential energy** is the energy something gains if you lift it up. You work it out using: $\Delta E_p = mg\Delta h$, where m is the mass of the object, Δh is the height it is lifted and g is the gravitational field strength (9.81 Nkg^{-1} on Earth).

4) **Elastic potential energy** (elastic stored energy) is the energy you get in, say, a stretched rubber band or spring. You work this out using $E = \frac{1}{2}ke^2$, where e is the extension of the spring and k is the stiffness constant.

Examples

These pictures show you three **examples** of changes between kinetic and potential energy.

1) As Becky throws the **ball upwards**, **kinetic energy** is converted into **gravitational potential energy**. When it **comes down** again, that **gravitational potential** energy is **converted back** into **kinetic** energy.

2) As Dominic goes **down the slide**, **gravitational potential energy** is converted to **kinetic energy**.

3) As Simon bounces upwards from the trampoline, **elastic potential energy** is converted to **kinetic energy**, to **gravitational potential energy**. As he comes back down again, that **gravitational potential** energy is **converted back** to **kinetic** energy, to **elastic potential** energy, and so on.

In **real life** there are also **frictional forces** — Simon would have to use some **force** from his **muscles** to keep **jumping** to the **same height** above the trampoline each time. Each time the trampoline **stretches**, some **heat** is generated in the trampoline material. You're usually told to **ignore friction** in exam questions — this means you can **assume** that the **only forces** are those that provide the **potential or kinetic energy** (in this example that's **Simon's weight** and the **tension** in the springs and trampoline material). If you're ignoring friction, you can say that the **sum of the kinetic and potential energies is constant**.

Conservation of Energy

Use Conservation of Energy to **Solve Problems**

You need to be able to **use** conservation of mechanical energy (change in potential energy = change in kinetic energy) to solve problems. The classic example is the **simple pendulum**.

In a simple pendulum, you assume that all the mass is in the **bob** at the end.

Example

A simple pendulum has a mass of 700 g and a length of 50 cm. It is pulled out to an angle of 30° from the vertical.

(a) Find the gravitational potential energy stored in the pendulum bob.

Start by drawing a diagram.

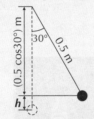

You can work out the increase in height, **h**, of the end of the pendulum using trig.

Gravitational potential energy = **mgh**
= 0.7 × 9.81 × (0.5 – 0.5 cos30°)
= 0.46 J

(b) The pendulum is released. Find the maximum speed of the pendulum bob as it passes the vertical position.

To find the *maximum* speed, assume no air resistance, then **mgh** = ½**mv**².

So $\frac{1}{2}mv^2 = 0.46$

rearrange to find $v = \sqrt{\dfrac{2 \times 0.46}{0.7}} = 1.15$ ms⁻¹

OR

Cancel the **m**s and rearrange to give:
$v^2 = 2gh$
= 2 × 9.81 × (0.5 – 0.5 cos30°)
= 1.31429...
v = 1.15 ms⁻¹

You could be asked to apply this stuff to just about any situation in the exam. **Rollercoasters** are a bit of a favourite.

Practice Questions

Q1   State the principle of conservation of energy.

Q2   What are the equations for calculating kinetic energy and gravitational potential energy?

Q3   Show that, if there's no air resistance and the mass of the string is negligible, the speed of a pendulum is independent of the mass of the bob.

Exam Questions

Q1   A skateboarder is on a half-pipe. He lets the board run down one side of the ramp and up the other.
The height of the ramp is 2 m. Take **g** as 9.81 Nkg⁻¹.

(a) If you assume that there is no friction, what would be his speed at the lowest point of the ramp?   [3 marks]

(b) How high will he rise up the other side?   [1 mark]

(c) Real ramps are not frictionless, so what must the skater do to reach the top on the other side?   [1 mark]

Q2   A 20 g rubber ball is released from a height of 8 m. (Assume that the effect of air resistance is negligible.)

(a) Find the kinetic energy of the ball just before it hits the ground.   [2 marks]

(b) The ball strikes the ground and rebounds to a height of 6.5 m. How much energy is converted to heat and sound in the impact with the ground?   [2 marks]

Energy is never lost — it just sometimes prefers the scenic route...

Remember to check your answers — I can't count the number of times I've forgotten to square the velocities or to multiply by the ½... I reckon it's definitely worth the extra minute to check.

Hooke's Law

These pages are for AQA A Unit 2, Edexcel Unit 1, OCR A Unit 1 and OCR B Unit 1.

Hooke's law doesn't apply to all materials, and only works for the rest up to a point, but it's still pretty handy.

Hooke's Law Says that Extension is Proportional to Force

If a **metal wire** is supported at the top and then a weight attached to the bottom, it **stretches**. The weight pulls down with force **F**, producing an equal and opposite force at the support.

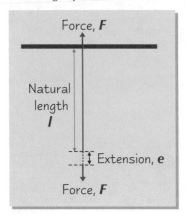

1) **Robert Hooke** discovered in 1676 that the extension of a stretched wire, **e**, is proportional to the load or force, **F**. This relationship is now called **Hooke's law**.

2) Hooke's law can be written:

$$F = ke$$

Where **k** is a constant that depends on the material being stretched. **k** is called the **stiffness constant**.

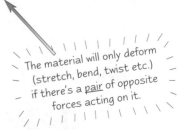

The material will only deform (stretch, bend, twist etc.) if there's a <u>pair</u> of opposite forces acting on it.

I'm a bit irrelevant on this page — bungee ropes don't obey Hooke's Law... Do you think I need to get out more?

Hooke's law Also Applies to Springs

A metal spring also changes length when you apply a **pair of opposite forces**.

1) The **extension** or **compression** of a spring is **proportional** to the **force** applied — so Hooke's law applies.

2) For springs, **k** in the formula **F = ke** is usually called the **spring stiffness** or **spring constant**.

> Hooke's law works just as well for **compressive** forces as **tensile** forces. For a spring, **k** has the **same value** whether the forces are tensile or compressive (that's not true for all materials).

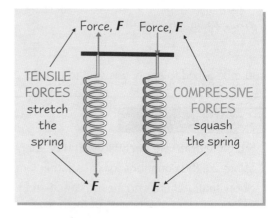

Hooke's law Stops Working when the Load is Great Enough

There's a **limit** to the force you can apply for Hooke's law to stay true.

1) The graph shows load against extension for a **typical metal wire**.

2) The first part of the graph shows Hooke's law being obeyed — there's a **straight-line relationship** between **load** and **extension**.

3) When the load becomes great enough, the graph starts to **curve**. The point marked E on the graph is called the **elastic limit**.

4) If you increase the load past the elastic limit, the material will be **permanently stretched**. When all the force is removed, the material will be **longer** than at the start.

5) **Metals** generally obey Hooke's law up to the limit of proportionality (see p.41), which is very near the elastic limit.

6) Be careful — there are some materials, like **rubber**, that only obey Hooke's law for **really small** extensions.

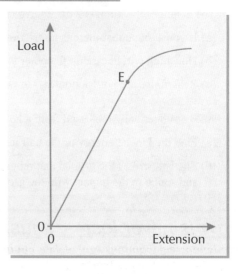

Hooke's Law

So basically...

A Stretch can be *Elastic* or *Plastic*

Elastic

If a **deformation** is **elastic**, the material returns to its **original shape** once the forces are removed.

1) When the material is put under **tension**, the **atoms** of the material are **pulled apart** from one another.

2) Atoms can **move** small distances relative to their **equilibrium positions**, without actually changing position in the material.

3) Once the **load** is **removed**, the atoms **return** to their **equilibrium** distance apart.

For a metal, elastic deformation happens as long as **Hooke's law** is obeyed.

Plastic

If a deformation is **plastic**, the material is **permanently stretched**.

1) Some atoms in the material move position relative to one another.

2) When the load is removed, the **atoms don't return** to their original positions.

A metal stretched **past its elastic limit** shows plastic deformation.

Brittle materials (e.g. glass, perspex, cast iron, chocolate chip cookies... mmmm... cookies) **don't** tend to behave plastically. They **fracture** before they reach the elastic limit.

Practice Questions

Q1 State Hooke's law.

Q2 Define tensile forces and compressive forces.

Q3 Explain what is meant by the elastic limit of a material.

Q4 From studying the force-extension graph for a material as it is loaded and unloaded, how can you tell:
(a) if Hooke's law is being obeyed,
(b) if the elastic limit has been reached?

Q5 What is plastic behaviour of a material under load?

Exam Questions

Q1 A metal guitar string stretches 4.0 mm when a 10 N force is applied.

(a) If the string obeys Hooke's law, how far will the string stretch with a 15 N force? [1 mark]

(b) Calculate the stiffness constant for this string in Nm^{-1}. [2 marks]

(c) The string is tightened beyond its elastic limit. What would be noticed about the string? [1 mark]

Q2 A rubber band is 6.0 cm long. When it is loaded with 2.5 N, its length becomes 10.4 cm. Further loading increases the length to 16.2 cm when the force is 5.0 N.

Does the rubber band obey Hooke's law when the force on it is 5.0 N?
Justify your answer with a suitable calculation. [2 marks]

Sod's Law — if you don't learn it, it'll be in the exam...

Okay, so this isn't the most riveting stuff in the world — but at least it's fairly simple. I promise you, Physics does get more interesting than this. You always get the boring stuff near the beginning of a book.
Wait till page 92 — you'll be longing for a bit of 17th century tedium then. Come back Hooke —all is forgiven.

Stress and Strain

These pages are for AQA A Unit 2, Edexcel Unit 1, OCR A Unit 1 and OCR B Unit 1.

How much a material stretches for a particular applied force depends on its dimensions.
If you want to compare the properties of two different materials, you need to use stress and strain instead.
A stress-strain graph is the same for any sample of a particular material — the size of the sample doesn't matter.

A Stress Causes a Strain

A material subjected to a pair of **opposite forces** might **deform**, i.e. **change shape**. If the forces
stretch the material, they're **tensile**. If the forces **squash** the material, they're **compressive**.

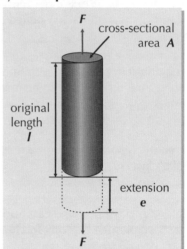

1) **Tensile stress** is defined as the **force applied**, *F*,
   divided by the **cross-sectional area**, *A*:

$$\text{stress} = \frac{F}{A}$$

   The **units** of stress are **Nm⁻²** or pascals, **Pa**.

2) **Tensile strain** is defined as the **change in length**, i.e. the
   extension, divided by the **original length** of the material:

$$\text{strain} = \frac{e}{l}$$

   Strain has **no units** — it's just a **number**.

3) It doesn't matter whether the forces producing the **stress** and
   strain are **tensile** or **compressive** — the **same equations** apply.
   The only difference is that you tend to think of **tensile** forces as **positive**, and **compressive** forces as **negative**.

A Stress Big Enough to Break the Material is Called the Breaking Stress

As a greater and greater tensile **force** is applied to a material, the **stress** on it **increases**.

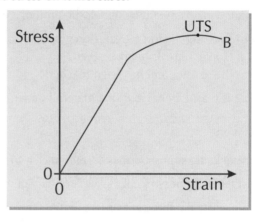

1) The effect of the **stress** is to start to **pull**
   the **atoms apart** from one another.

2) Eventually the stress becomes **so great** that atoms
   separate completely, and the **material breaks**.
   This is shown by point **B** on the graph.
   The stress at which this occurs is called
   the **breaking stress** (or **fracture stress**).

3) The point marked **UTS** on the graph is
   called the **ultimate tensile stress**. This is the
   maximum stress that the material can withstand.

4) **Engineers** have to consider the **UTS** and **breaking**
   stress of materials when designing a **structure**.

"Strain energy" is just for AQA A, Edexcel and OCR A, so if you're doing OCR B you can skip straight to the questions.

Elastic Strain Energy is the Energy Stored in a Stretched Material

When a material is **stretched**, **work** has to be done
in stretching the material.

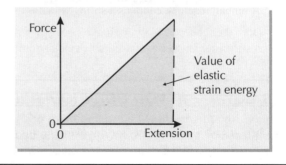

1) **Before** the **elastic limit**, all the **work done** in stretching
   is **stored** as **potential energy** in the material.

2) This stored energy is called **elastic strain energy**.

3) On a **graph** of **force against extension**, the elastic
   strain energy is given by the **area under the graph**.

Stress and Strain

You can Calculate the Energy Stored in a Stretched Wire

Provided a material obeys Hooke's law, the **potential energy** stored inside it can be **calculated** quite easily.

1) The work done on the wire in stretching it is equal to the energy stored.

2) **Work done** equals **force × displacement**.

3) However, the **force** on the material **isn't constant**. It rises from zero up to force F.
   To calculate the **work done**, use the average force between zero and F, i.e. $\frac{1}{2}F$.

   work done $= \frac{1}{2}F \times e$

4) Then the **elastic strain energy**, E, is: *This is the triangular area under the force-extension graph — see previous page.*

   $E = \frac{1}{2}Fe$

5) Because Hooke's law is being obeyed, $F = ke$,
   which means F can be replaced in the equation to give:

   $E = \frac{1}{2}ke^2$

6) If the material is stretched beyond the **elastic limit**, some work is done separating atoms.
   This will **not** be **stored** as strain energy and so isn't available when the force is released.

Practice Questions

Q1 Write a definition for tensile stress.

Q2 Explain what is meant by the tensile strain on a material.

Q3 What is meant by the breaking stress of a material?

Q4 How can the elastic strain energy be found from the force against extension graph of a material under load?

Q5 The work done is usually calculated as force multiplied by displacement.
   Explain why the work done in stretching a wire is $\frac{1}{2}Fe$.

Exam Questions

Q1 A steel wire is 2.00 m long. When a 300 N force is applied to the wire, it stretches 4.0 mm.
   The wire has a circular cross-section with a diameter of 1.0 mm.

   (a) What is the cross-sectional area of the wire?   [1 mark]

   (b) Calculate the tensile stress in the wire.   [1 mark]

   (c) Calculate the tensile strain of the wire.   [1 mark]

Q2 A copper wire (which obeys Hooke's law) is stretched by 3.0 mm when a force of 50 N is applied.

   (a) Calculate the stiffness constant for this wire in Nm^{-1}.   [2 marks]

   (b) What is the value of the elastic strain energy in the stretched wire?   [1 mark]

Q3 A pinball machine contains a spring which is used to fire a small, 12 g metal ball to start the game.
   The spring has a stiffness constant of $40.8\ Nm^{-1}$. It is compressed by 5 cm and then released to fire the ball.

   Calculate the maximum possible speed of the ball.   [4 marks]

UTS a laugh a minute, this stuff...

Here endeth the proper physics for this section — the rest of it's materials science (and I don't care what your exam boards say). It's all a bit "useful" for my liking. Calls itself a physics course... grumble... grumble... wasn't like this in my day... But to be fair — some of it's quite interesting, and there are some pretty pictures coming up on page 40.

The Young Modulus

These pages are for AQA A Unit 2, Edexcel Unit 1, OCR A Unit 1 and OCR B Unit 1.

Busy chap, Thomas Young. He did this work on tensile stress as something of a sideline. Light was his main thing. He proved that light behaved like a wave, explained how we see in colour and worked out what causes astigmatism.

The **Young Modulus** is Stress ÷ Strain

When you apply a **load** to stretch a material, it experiences a **tensile stress** and a **tensile strain**.

1) Up to a point called the **limit of proportionality** (see p.41), the stress and strain of a material are proportional to each other.

2) So below this limit, for a particular material, stress divided by strain is a constant. This constant is called the **Young modulus**, *E*.

$$E = \frac{\text{tensile stress}}{\text{tensile strain}} = \frac{F/A}{e/l} = \frac{Fl}{eA}$$

Where, *F* = force in N, *A* = cross-sectional area in m², *l* = initial length in m and *e* = extension in m.

3) The **units** of the Young modulus are the same as stress (**Nm⁻²** or pascals), since strain has no units.

4) The Young modulus is used by **engineers** to make sure their materials can withstand sufficient forces.

To **Find** the Young Modulus, You need a **Very Long Wire**

This is the experiment you're most likely to do in class:

Mum moment: if you're doing this experiment, wear safety goggles — if the wire snaps, it could get very messy...

The Young Modulus

wire fixed at one end · test wire · marker · pulley · bench · rule with mm markings · weights

The test wire should be thin, and as long as possible. The **longer and thinner** the wire, the more it **extends** for the same force.

Start with the **smallest weight** necessary to straighten the wire.

Measure the **distance** between the **fixed end of the wire** and the **marker** — this is your unstretched length.

If you then increase the weight, the **wire stretches** and the **marker moves**.

Increase the **weight** by steps, recording the marker reading each time — the **extension** is the **difference** between this reading and the **unstretched length**.

Once you've taken all your readings, use a **micrometer** to measure the **diameter** of the wire in several places. Take an average of your measurements, and use that to work out the average **cross-sectional area** of the wire.

The other standard way of measuring the Young modulus in the lab is using **Searle's apparatus**. This is a bit more accurate, but it's harder to do and the equipment's more complicated.

The Young Modulus

Use a *Stress-Strain Graph* to Find **E**

You can plot a **graph** of **stress against strain** from your results.

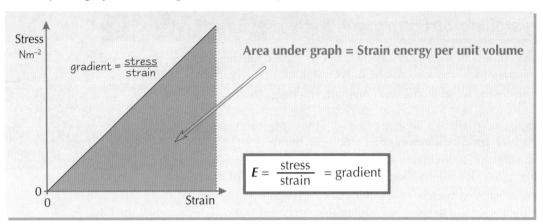

1) The **gradient** of the graph gives the Young modulus, **E**.

2) The **area under the graph** gives the **strain energy** (or energy stored) per unit volume i.e. the energy stored per 1 m³ of wire.

3) The stress-strain graph is a **straight line** provided that Hooke's law is obeyed, so you can also calculate the energy per unit volume as:

Again, if you're doing OCR B you can ignore the energy bits.

energy = ½ × stress × strain

Practice Questions

Q1 Define the Young modulus for a material.

Q2 What are the units for the Young modulus?

Q3 Explain why a thin test wire is used to find the Young modulus.

Q4 What is given by the area contained under a stress-strain graph?

Exam Questions

Q1 A steel wire is stretched elastically. For a load of 80 N, the wire extends by 3.6 mm. The original length of the wire was 2.50 m and its average diameter is 0.6 mm.

(a) Calculate the cross-sectional area of the wire in m². [1 mark]

(b) Find the tensile stress applied to the wire. [1 mark]

(c) Calculate the tensile strain of the wire. [1 mark]

(d) What is the value of the Young modulus for steel? [1 mark]

Q2 The Young modulus for copper is 1.3×10^{11} Nm⁻².

(a) If the stress on a copper wire is 2.6×10^8 Nm⁻², what is the strain? [2 marks]

(b) If the load applied to the copper wire is 100 N, what is the cross-sectional area of the wire? [1 mark]

(c) Calculate the strain energy per unit volume for this loaded wire. [1 mark]

Learn that experiment — it's important...

Getting back to the good Dr Young... As if ground-breaking work in light, the physics of vision and materials science wasn't enough, he was also a well-respected physician, a linguist and an Egyptologist. He was one of the first to try to decipher the Rosetta stone (he didn't get it right, but nobody's perfect). Makes you feel kind of inferior, doesn't it. Best get learning.

Structures of Solids

These pages are for OCR B Unit 1 only.

The reason materials are flexible or tough is down to their structure.
When the going gets tough, the tough get going to page 40 to look up the definition of tough...

Metals — a *Crystalline Structure* with a 'Sea' of *Free Electrons*

1) The atoms in a metal usually form a **crystalline** lattice — where the metal atoms are arranged in a **regular repeating pattern**. (They can also be **polycrystalline** — see below).

2) The outer electrons of the metal atoms don't need much energy to be able to desert their atoms in this crystalline structure. They form a 'sea' of **free electrons,** leaving behind a lattice of ions. It's these free electrons that make metals such **good conductors** of heat and electricity.

metal ion

'sea' of free electrons

3) The electrostatic attraction between the ion lattice and the free electrons forms the metallic bond. It's these **strong** bonds that make metals **stiff** materials.

4) The strongly bonded lattice structure of a metal makes it **tough**. The ions within the lattice can **move** when you apply a force to the metal — making it **ductile**.

Ceramics — *Giant Rigid Structures*

1) Ceramics like **pottery**, **brick** and **glass** are made by melting certain materials, and then letting them cool.

2) The arrangement of atoms in a ceramic can be **crystalline** or **polycrystalline** — where there are many regions (or **grains**) of crystalline structure. The atoms in each grain line up in a different direction.

MANFRED KAGE / SCIENCE PHOTO LIBRARY

3) Some ceramics like **glass** are **amorphous** — there's no overall pattern; the atoms are arranged at **random**. The quicker a molten ceramic material is cooled, the more likely it is to be amorphous.

4) However they're arranged, the atoms in a ceramic are either **ionically** or **covalently** bonded in a **giant rigid structure**. The **strong bonds** between the atoms make ceramics **stiff**, while the **rigid** structure means that ceramics are very **brittle** materials.

Polymers — *Lots* of Monomers Joined Together

1) A **polymer** is a molecular **chain**, made up of a **single repeating unit** called a **monomer**.

2) You get **natural** polymers like rubber, as well as a whole host of **man-made** ones like polythene.

3) The monomers in a polymer chain are **covalently** bonded together, and so are very hard to separate. This means even the thin polymer material used to make carrier bags is still pretty **strong**.

4) The polymer chains are often scrunched up or folded, and can unfold by **rotating** about their bonds when you pull them. This is what makes polymer materials **flexible**. The more easily the monomers can rotate, the more flexible the polymer will be.

monomer

monomers can rotate about their bonds

5) The strength and number of bonds **between** the chains also affect a polymer's flexibility. The stronger the cross-linking bonds, and the more cross-linking bonds you've got, the more **rigid** the material.

Composites — *Combine* the Properties of *Different Materials*

Composites are a bit like a pick 'n' mix — you combine two different materials to get a material with the properties you want.

One of the most common composites is **reinforced concrete**. Normal concrete is really **strong** when you try to **compress** it, but is **brittle** under any sort of **tension** force, like when being bent. Obviously if you're making a building out of concrete, using a brittle material wouldn't be too great an idea. To increase the strength of the concrete structure under tension, you embed **steel rods** into it. Ta da... reinforced concrete.

Structures of Solids

You Can Use *Electron Microscope Images* to *Estimate* the *Size* of *Atoms*

1) There are loads of different ways you can look at the structure of a material.

2) You can use powerful **optical microscopes** to get a good view of the surface of a material.

3) **Scanning Electron Microscopes** (**SEM**) and **Atomic Force Microscopes** (**AFM**) don't let you see a material's surface directly, but can be used to build up an atom-by-atom image of the surface on a computer screen.

4) You can use images like this to estimate and measure the size of the atoms in a material. Each 'blob' shows the size and position of an individual atom in the regular lattice. By knowing the width shown by the image, you can work out the width of an atom.

Example

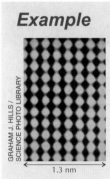

GRAHAM J. HILLS / SCIENCE PHOTO LIBRARY

1.3 nm

The figure shows a high-resolution transmission electron micrograph (HREM) image of a thin gold lattice. The field of view shown by this image is 1.3 nm. Estimate the typical size of a gold atom.

The width of this gold image is roughly 7 atoms and the width shown by the image is 1.3 nm — so you can find a rough size of a gold atom by dividing the width of the image by how many atoms it is across.

The distance from atom centre to atom centre = $1.3 \div 7 = $ **0.19 nm**.

5) Microscope images only ever show you the **surface** of a material — the structure underneath might be **completely different**. You need techniques like **X-ray crystallography** to really see how the atoms in a material are arranged.

Practice Questions

Q1 Describe the structure of a typical metal.

Q2 Describe the arrangement of atoms in an amorphous solid.

Q3 What is a polymer? Give one factor that affects how rigid a polymer material is.

Q4 Write down one technique that can show the atomic arrangement of a substance on its surface.

Exam Questions

Q1 Give one example of a composite material.
State an application for your chosen material.
Write down one advantage of using this composite material over a non-composite. [3 marks]

Q2 The figure shows a Scanning Tunnelling Microscope (STM) image of a layer of metal atoms.
The field of view shown by the height of the image is 4.05 nm.
Estimate the average size of the atoms shown.

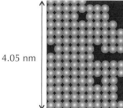

4.05 nm

[2 marks]

And that's why shops don't make their bags out of clay...

It's like what Trisha's been saying all along — it's what's on the inside that counts... and it's no different for bricks. Make sure you get to grips with the structure of each class of materials so you can explain why hard materials are hard, why floppy materials flop, and why it wouldn't be such a great idea to make a glass bungee cord...

Behaviour of Solids

These pages are for Edexcel Unit 1, OCR A Unit 1 and OCR B Unit 1.
If you're doing OCR A, you only need the definitions of brittle and ductile. Otherwise you need all six... lucky you.

Terms to Describe the *Behaviour of Solids* Have *Precise Meanings*

Brittle materials break suddenly without deforming plastically.

If you apply a **force** to a **brittle material**, it won't **deform plastically** (see p 33), but will suddenly **snap** when the force gets to a certain size. Brittle materials can also be quite **weak** if they have **cracks** in them.

A **chocolate bar** is an example of a brittle material — you can break chunks of chocolate off the bar without the whole thing changing shape. **Ceramics** (e.g. **glass** and **pottery**) are brittle too — they tend to shatter.

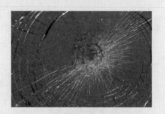

Ductile materials can be drawn into wires without losing their strength.

You can change the **shape** of **ductile materials** by drawing them into **wires** or other shapes. The important thing is that they **keep their strength** when they're deformed like this. **Copper** is ductile, and with its high electrical conductivity this means that it's ideal for **electric wires**. A **ductile material** has been used for the cables supporting the **ski lift** in the photo — it's been drawn into long wires, but kept its strength.

Malleable materials change shape but may lose their strength.

The shape of **malleable materials** can be changed fairly easily, e.g. by **hammering** or **rolling**. The difference between malleable and ductile materials is that **malleable** materials **won't** necessarily **keep their strength**.

Gold is an example of a malleable metal — you can change the shape of a gold ring using just your fingers. **Brass** is malleable too — it can be bent and stretched into **complex shapes** to make musical instruments.

Hard materials are very resistant to cutting, indentation and abrasion.

If you try to cut, dent or scratch a hard material, you'll probably have very little effect. Their structure means **hard materials** are **resistant** to **cutting**, **indentation** (becoming dented) and **abrasion** (scratching).

Cutting tools (e.g. chisels) need to be harder than the stuff they're cutting — they're often made from **hardened steel**. **Diamond** is just about the hardest material there is — it's often used to reinforce the tips of drill bits.

Stiff materials have a high resistance to bending and stretching.

Changing the shape of **stiff materials** is really difficult as they are **resistant** to both **bending** and **stretching**. Stiffness is measured by the **Young modulus** (see p. 36) — the higher the value, the stiffer the material.

The outer protective casing of **safety helmets** and **safety boots** need to be very stiff so that they keep their shape and don't **crush** onto your body when something impacts on them.

Tough materials are really difficult to break.

Toughness is a measure of the **energy** a material can **absorb** before it breaks. Really **tough materials** can absorb a lot of energy so are very **difficult** to **break**. Some **polymers**, including certain types of **polythene**, are very tough. The hull of this **kayak** is made of a tough material so it won't break on rocks.

Behaviour of Solids

Do you remember that lovely stress-strain graph from page 34? Well, it turns out that because different solids have different properties, their stress-strain graphs look different too.

Stress-Strain Graphs for Ductile Materials Curve

The diagram shows a **stress-strain graph** for a typical **ductile** material — e.g. a copper wire.

Point **Y** is the **yield point** — here the material suddenly starts to **stretch** without any extra load. The **yield point** (or yield stress) is the **stress** at which a large amount of **plastic deformation** takes place with a **constant** or **reduced load**.

Point **E** is the **elastic limit** — at this point the material starts to behave **plastically**. From point E onwards, the material would **no longer** return to its **original shape** once the stress was removed.

Point **P** is the **limit of proportionality** — after this, the graph is no longer a straight line but starts to **bend**. At this point, the material **stops** obeying **Hooke's law**, but would still **return** to its **original shape** if the stress was removed.

Before point **P**, the graph is a **straight line** through the **origin**. This shows that the material is obeying **Hooke's law** (page 32).

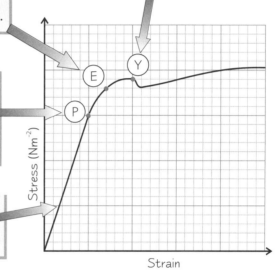

Those of you doing Edexcel or OCR B can go straight to the questions now. The rest is for OCR A only.

Stress-Strain Graphs for Brittle Materials Don't Curve

The stress-strain graph above is typical of a copper wire. However, other materials (including other metals) have very **different** stress-strain graphs. The graph shown below is typical of a **brittle** material.

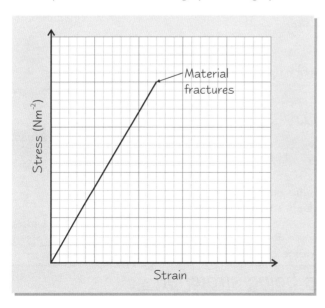

The graph starts the same as the one above — with a **straight line through the origin**. So brittle materials also obey **Hooke's law**.

However, when the **stress** reaches a certain point, the material **snaps** — it doesn't deform plastically.

When **stress** is applied to a brittle material any **tiny cracks** at the material's surface get **bigger** and **bigger** until the material **breaks** completely. This is called **brittle fracture**.

The **cracks** in **brittle** materials can **grow** because they have a **rigid structure** (see page 38). **Copper** is not brittle because the **ions** within it can **move** to **prevent** any **cracks** getting bigger.

Hooke's law — it's the pirates' code... yarr

Behaviour of Solids

I hope the stresses and strains of this section aren't getting to you too much. Don't worry, though — there's just this page to go before you're on to the slippy sloppy world of fluids — including an experiment based on honey... mmm

Rubber and Polythene Are Polymeric Materials

1) The **molecules** that make up **polymeric** (or polymer) **materials** are arranged in **long chains**.

2) They have a **range** of properties, so different polymers have different **stress-strain graphs**. The diagram below shows two examples — **rubber** and **polythene**.

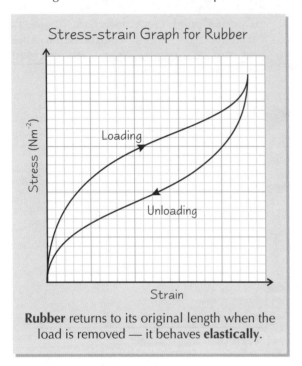

Rubber returns to its original length when the load is removed — it behaves **elastically**.

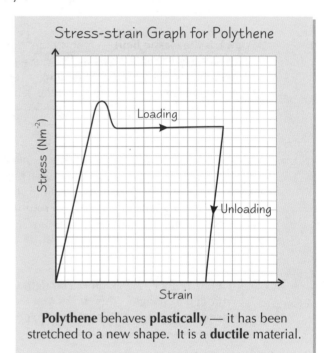

Polythene behaves **plastically** — it has been stretched to a new shape. It is a **ductile** material.

Practice Questions

Q1 Write short definitions of the following terms: ductile, stiff, tough, brittle.

Q2 What is the difference between the limit of proportionality and the elastic limit?

Q3 Sketch stress-strain graphs of typical ductile, brittle and polymeric materials and describe their shapes.

Exam Questions

Q1 Hardened steel is a hard, brittle form of steel made by heating it up slowly and then quenching it in cold water.

    (a) What is meant by the terms *hard* and *brittle*? [2 marks]

    (b) Write down one application in which hardened steel could be used.
        Explain why it would be useful in this context. [2 marks]

    (c) Sketch a stress-strain graph for hardened steel. [2 marks]

Q2 Riding helmets are designed to protect a rider's head from injury should they fall off their horse.
Describe three properties of a material that would be suitable for a riding helmet.
Explain why each of these properties is advantageous. [6 marks]

My brain must be stiff — it's resistant to being stretched...

Those material scientists are a tricky lot — you go all your life thinking you know what hard means (who doesn't?), then they come along and say, 'that's not good enough — you need to know the proper meaning'. They've got a point though — saying, 'hard... well, it's err... not soft' isn't going to get you any marks. Go on — learn them all. It'll be good fun... honest.

Properties of Fluids

These pages are for Edexcel Unit 1 only.

Solids are quite good fun, but you're in for a treat now — it's time to learn all about fluids...

Streamlines are Stable Flowlines

1) **Fluids** are things that **flow** — i.e. **liquids** and **gases**.

2) When a fluid flows, **different parts** of it may move in **different directions** and at **different rates**. It's useful to think of a fluid as made up of '**fluid elements**'. A **fluid element** is a part of the fluid in which all the particles are flowing in the **same direction** at the **same rate** — i.e. with the **same velocity**.

3) Each fluid element is **small** enough that it flows **without breaking up**, but **large** enough that you don't have to consider the **random movement** (thermal motion) of the **particles** within it.

4) The **path** that a particular **fluid element** follows is called a **flowline**.

5) If **every element** on a flowline follows the **same path**, then the flowline is said to be **stable** because it does not move about. A **stable flowline** is called a **streamline**.

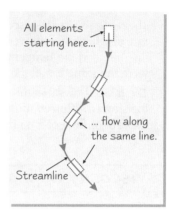

All elements starting here...

... flow along the same line.

Streamline

Streamlines Are Parallel in Laminar Flow

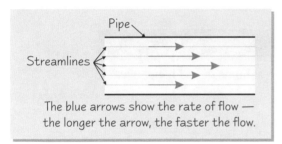

Pipe

Streamlines

The blue arrows show the rate of flow — the longer the arrow, the faster the flow.

1) **Laminar flow** is a flow **pattern** where all the **fluid elements** flow in the **same direction**.

2) The result of this is that all the flowlines are **streamlines** that run **parallel** to each another.

3) **Laminar flow** usually occurs when a fluid is **flowing slowly**.

4) The diagram shows water undergoing **laminar flow** in a **pipe**. The streamlines **all** run along the length of the pipe.

Flowlines Are Unstable in Turbulent Flow

1) **Turbulent flow** is a different flow **pattern** where the **fluid elements** get **mixed up**. You can't draw **streamlines** if the flow is turbulent because the flowlines are **unstable** (keep changing).

2) **Turbulent flow** usually occurs when a **fluid** is flowing **quickly**.

3) In turbulent flow, the fluid often moves around in **miniature whirlpools** — called **eddy currents**.

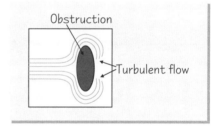

Obstruction

Turbulent flow

Both types of flow (laminar and turbulent) are used in **manufacturing**. For example, **laminar flow** is needed if the fluid is to flow **smoothly** (e.g. through pipes) and with a **minimum** amount of **viscous drag** (see below). **Turbulent flow** is needed if fluids need to be thoroughly **mixed** (e.g. mixing chemicals or ingredients).

Viscous Drag — the Force of Friction Produced by a Flowing Fluid

1) When fluid elements move **past** each other with **different velocities** there is a **force of friction** between them. Friction opposes motion, so the force acts to **slow** the flow.

2) The **force of friction** produced by a flowing fluid is called **viscous drag**.

3) The **size** of the force depends on the **viscosity** of the fluid — the **higher the viscosity**, the **larger the force**.

4) **Viscous drag** is much **larger** when the flow is **turbulent**.

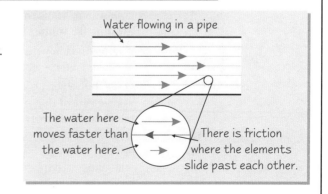

Water flowing in a pipe

The water here moves faster than the water here.

There is friction where the elements slide past each other.

Properties of Fluids

Rate of Flow Depends on Viscosity

The table shows the **viscosity** of four different fluids and the **rate** at which they **flowed** through a pipe. The **diameter** of the pipe and the **temperature** and **pressure** within the pipe were the **same** for all the fluids.

The table shows that the **higher the viscosity** of a fluid, the **slower it flowed** through the pipe. In other words, the **rate of flow** of a fluid **depends** on its **viscosity**.

Fluid	Viscosity (Nsm^{-2})	Rate of flow $(\text{m}^3\text{s}^{-1})$
Gasoline	2.8×10^{-4}	2.72
Water	1.1×10^{-3}	0.83
Kerosene	2.0×10^{-3}	0.68
Crude oil	9.8×10^{-3}	0.08

Viscosity Depends on Temperature

The **viscosities** given in the table above were all measured at the **same temperature**. This is important because the **viscosity** of a fluid **changes** with its **temperature**.

1)   The **viscosity** of most fluids **decreases** as the **temperature increases**.

2)   This means fluids generally **flow faster** if they're **hotter**.

The mud was more viscous than Humphrey had realised.

You Can Measure How Temperature Affects the Viscosity of a Fluid

You might try this experiment in class — or you could do it in the kitchen at home (if you happen to have a dropping funnel to hand):

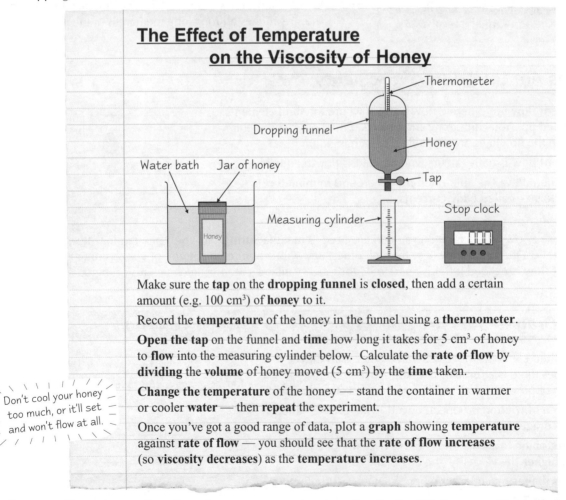

The Effect of Temperature on the Viscosity of Honey

Make sure the **tap** on the **dropping funnel** is **closed**, then add a certain amount (e.g. 100 cm³) of **honey** to it.

Record the **temperature** of the honey in the funnel using a **thermometer**.

Open the tap on the funnel and **time** how long it takes for 5 cm³ of honey to **flow** into the measuring cylinder below. Calculate the **rate of flow** by **dividing** the **volume** of honey moved (5 cm³) by the **time** taken.

Change the temperature of the honey — stand the container in warmer or cooler **water** — then **repeat** the experiment.

Once you've got a good range of data, plot a **graph** showing **temperature** against **rate of flow** — you should see that the **rate of flow increases** (so **viscosity decreases**) as the **temperature increases**.

Don't cool your honey too much, or it'll set and won't flow at all.

Another way of investigating the effect of temperature on the viscosity of a liquid is to use an **Ostwald viscometer** to measure the **viscosity** of the liquid at different **temperatures** — if you've got one handy of course.

Properties of Fluids

Viscous Drag Acts on Objects Moving Through Fluids

When an object moves through a fluid, you get **friction** between the surface of the **object** and the **fluid**.
This is **viscous drag** — it's the same effect as the friction between fluid elements that move past each other (p. 43).
You can calculate the **force due to viscous drag** on a **spherical** object moving through a fluid using **Stokes' law**.

Stokes' law can be written as:

$$F = 6\pi\eta rv$$

F is the **viscous drag** (N), η (eta) is the **viscosity** of the fluid (Nsm^{-2} or Pa·s), *r* is the **radius** of the object (m) and *v* is the **speed** the object is moving at (ms^{-1}).

Fluids Exert Upthrust on Immersed Objects

1) When you **float** an object on water, the **weight** of the object is **balanced** by an **opposing force** from the water. If you try to push the object under the water, it will **spring back** to the surface as soon as you let go. The **force** that 'pushes' the object **upwards** is called **upthrust** — it's caused by **fluid pressure**.

2) **Fluid pressure** is an **outward force** exerted on all **surfaces** the fluid is in contact with — including the surfaces of anything **immersed** in it. It's **caused** by the **weight** of the fluid — which means it **increases** with depth. The **deeper** you go into the fluid, the **greater** the **weight** of fluid above you, so the **greater** the **pressure**.

3) The result is that the **fluid pressure** is **higher** at the **bottom** of the object than at the top. This difference in pressure results in a **net upward force** on the object, as shown in the diagram. This force is the **upthrust**.

4) The size of the **upthrust** is **equal** to the **weight** of the **fluid displaced** by the object — this is **Archimedes' principle** and it's true for **all fluids**.

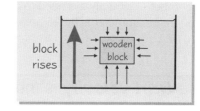

Upthrust = weight of fluid displaced

Practice Questions

Q1   What is a streamline?

Q2   What is meant by laminar flow? Draw a streamline diagram of a fluid flowing in this way.

Q3   How does the rate of flow of a fluid depend on its viscosity?

Q4   How does the rate of flow of most fluids depend on their temperature?

Exam Questions

Q1   A student dropped a marble into a measuring cylinder full of water. The marble sank slowly to the bottom.

(a) Draw a diagram of the marble falling through the water and label the three forces that are acting on it.   [3 marks]

(b) If the marble was falling at constant speed then what was the resultant force acting on it?   [1 mark]

(c) Use the following data to work out the speed that the marble was falling (at its terminal velocity).
Radius of marble = 5.0×10^{-3} m   Mass of marble = 5×10^{-5} kg
Mass of water displaced = 2.1×10^{-5} kg   Gravitational field strength = 9.81 Nkg^{-1}.
Viscosity of water = 0.0011 Nsm^{-2} [6 marks]

Q2   When oil is piped over long distances, it tends to flow more slowly during the night than during the day. Explain why this happens.   [3 marks]

Finding viscosity a drag? You need upthrust — it's a real boost...

If you can read this you clearly haven't tried the investigation on the last page — or else you were smart enough to put the book away before you covered it in honey. Mmm... honey... Sorry where was I, oh yes, fluids — very important, learn it all.

Charge, Current and Potential Difference

These pages are for AQA A Unit 1, Edexcel Unit 2, OCR A Unit 2 and OCR B Unit 1.

You wouldn't reckon there was that much to know about electricity... just plug something in, and bosh — electricity. Ah well, never mind the age of innocence — here are all the gory details...

Current is the Rate of Flow of Charge

The **current** in a **wire** is like **water** flowing in a **pipe**. The **amount** of water that flows depends on the **flow rate** and the **time**. It's the same with electricity — **current is the rate of flow of charge**.

$$\Delta Q = I\Delta t \quad \text{or} \quad I = \frac{\Delta Q}{\Delta t}$$

Where ΔQ is the charge in coulombs,
I is the current and Δt is the time taken.

Remember that conventional current flows from + to -, the opposite way from electron flow.

The Coulomb is the Unit of Charge
One **coulomb** (**C**) is defined as the **amount of charge** that passes in **1 second** when the **current** is **1 ampere**.

For *OCR A* you need to know the elementary charge too (i.e. the charge on a single electron):
$$e = 1.6 \times 10^{-19} \text{ C}$$

You can measure the current flowing through a part of a circuit using an **ammeter**.
Remember — you always need to attach an ammeter in **series** (so that the current through the ammeter is the same as the current through the component — see page 56).

If you're doing AQA A or OCR B, you can skip straight to here.

The Drift Velocity is the Average Velocity of the Electrons   *Edexcel and OCR A*

When **current** flows through a wire, you might imagine the **electrons** all moving in the **same direction** in an orderly manner. Nope. In fact, they move **randomly** in **all directions**, but tend to **drift** one way. The **drift velocity** is just the **average velocity** and it's **much, much less** than the electrons' **actual speed**. (Their actual speed is about 10^6 ms^{-1}!)

The Current Depends on the Drift Velocity

The **current** is given by the equation: $I = nAvq$ You don't need to derive this for the exam but you do need to understand what it means.

where: I = electric current in A
       n = number of charge carriers per m³
       A = cross-sectional area in m²
       v = drift velocity in ms^{-1}
       q = charge in C carried by each charge carrier

See what the Equation Means by Changing One Variable at a Time

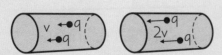
Double the number of charge carriers and the current doubles.

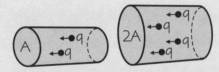
Doubling the area also doubles the current.

If the carriers move twice as fast you get twice the charge in the same time — twice the current.

Doubling the charge carried by each carrier means you get twice the charge in the same time — twice the current.

Charge, Current and Potential Difference

Different Materials have Different Numbers of Charge Carriers *Edexcel and OCR A*

1) In a **metal**, the **charge carriers** are **free electrons** — they're the ones from the **outer shell** of each atom. Thinking about the formula $I = nAvq$, there are **loads** of charge carriers, making n big. The **drift velocity** only needs to be **small**, even for a **high current**.

2) **Semiconductors** have **fewer charge carriers** than metals, so the **drift velocity** will need to be **higher** if you're going to have the **same current**.

3) A **perfect insulator** wouldn't have **any charge carriers**, so $n = 0$ in the formula and you'd get **no current**. **Real** insulators have a **very small** n.

Charge Carriers in Liquids and Gases are Ions

1) **Ionic crystals** like sodium chloride are **insulators**. Once **molten**, though, the liquid **conducts**. Positive and negative **ions** are the **charge carriers**. The **same thing** happens in an **ionic solution** like copper sulphate solution.

2) **Gases** are **insulators**, but if you apply a **high enough voltage** electrons get **ripped out** of atoms, giving you **ions** along a path. You get a **spark**.

Potential Difference is the Energy per Unit Charge

To make electric charge flow through a conductor, you need to do work on it. **Potential difference** (p.d.), or **voltage**, is defined as the **energy converted per unit charge moved**.

$$V = \frac{W}{Q}$$

W is the energy in joules. It's the work you do moving the charge.

Back to the 'water analogy' again. The p.d. is like the pressure that's forcing water along the pipe.

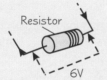
Resistor
6V

Here you do 6 J of work moving each coulomb of charge through the resistor, so the p.d. across it is 6 V. The energy gets converted to heat.

Definition of the Volt

The **potential difference** across a component is **1 volt** when you convert **1 joule** of energy moving **1 coulomb** of charge through the component.

$$1\,V = 1\,J\,C^{-1}$$

Practice Questions

Q1 Describe in words how current and charge are related.
Q2 Define the coulomb.
Q3 Explain what drift velocity is.
Q4 Define potential difference.

Exam Questions

Q1 A battery delivers 4500 C of electric charge to a circuit in 10 minutes. Calculate the average current. [2 marks]

Q2 Copper has 1.0×10^{29} free electrons per m^3. Calculate the drift velocity of the electrons in a copper wire of cross-sectional area $5.0 \times 10^{-6}\,m^2$ when it is carrying a current of 13 A. (electron charge $= 1.6 \times 10^{-19}\,C$) [3 marks]

Q3 An electric motor runs off a 12 V d.c. supply and has an overall efficiency of 75%. Calculate how much electric charge will pass through the motor when it does 90 J of work. [3 marks]

I can't even be bothered to make the current joke...

Talking of currant jokes, I saw this bottle of wine the other day called 'raisin d'être' — 'raison d'être' of course meaning 'reason for living', but spelled slightly different to make 'raisin', meaning 'grape'. Ho ho. Chuckled all the way out of Tesco.

Resistance and Conductance

These pages are for AQA A Unit 1, Edexcel Unit 2, OCR A Unit 2 and OCR B Units 1 and 2.

Everything has Resistance

1) If you put a **potential difference** (p.d.) across an **electrical component**, a **current** will flow.

2) **How much** current you get for a particular **p.d.** depends on the **resistance** of the component.

3) You can think of a component's **resistance** as a **measure** of how **difficult** it is to get a **current** to **flow** through it.

Mathematically, **resistance** is: $$R = \frac{V}{I}$$

This equation **defines** resistance.

For *OCR B Unit 1* you also need to know the formula for the **inverse** of resistance — **conductance, G.**

$$G = \frac{I}{V}$$

This is a measure of how good an electrical conductor a component is. It's measured in Ω^{-1} or siemens, S.

4) **Resistance** is measured in **ohms** (Ω).

A component has a resistance of **1 Ω** if a **potential difference** of **1 V** makes a **current** of **1 A** flow through it.

Three Things Determine Resistance

If you think about a nice, **simple electrical component**, like a **length of wire**, its **resistance** depends on:

1) **Length (l)**. The **longer** the wire the **more difficult** it is to make a **current flow**.

2) **Area (A)**. The **wider** the wire the **easier** it will be for the electrons to pass along it.

3) **Resistivity (ρ) depends on the **material**. The **structure** may make it easy or difficult for charge to flow. In general, resistivity depends on **environmental factors** as well, like **temperature** and **light intensity**.

The **resistivity** of a material is defined as the **resistance** of a **1 m length** with a **1 m^2 cross-sectional area**. It is measured in **ohm-metres** (Ωm).

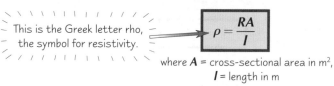

This is the Greek letter rho, the symbol for resistivity.

$$\rho = \frac{RA}{l}$$

where A = cross-sectional area in m^2, l = length in m

You'll more **usually** see the equation in the **form**: $$R = \rho \frac{l}{A}$$

And for *OCR B Unit 2* you need to know about the **inverse** again — **conductivity, σ.**

$$\sigma = \frac{Gl}{A} \qquad G = \sigma \frac{A}{l}$$

Typical values for the **resistivity** of **conductors** are **really small**, e.g., for **copper** (at 25 °C) $\rho = 1.72 \times 10^{-8}$ Ωm.

For an Ohmic Conductor, R is a Constant

A chap called **Ohm** did most of the early work on resistance. He developed a rule to **predict** how the **current** would **change** as the applied **potential difference** increased, for **certain types** of conductor. The rule is now called **Ohm's law** and the conductors that **obey** it (mostly metals) are called **ohmic conductors**.

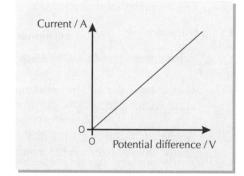

Provided the **temperature** is **constant**, the **current** through an ohmic conductor is **directly proportional** to the **potential difference** across it.

1) As you can see from the graph, **doubling** the **p.d. doubles** the **current**.

2) What this means is that the **resistance** is **constant**.

3) Often **factors** such as **light level** or **temperature** will have a **significant effect** on resistance (the resistivity changes), so you need to remember that Ohm's law is **only** true for **ohmic conductors** at **constant temperature**.

Resistance and Conductance

Superconductors Have Zero Resistivity   AQA A only

1) Normally, all materials have **some resistivity** — even really good conductors like silver and copper.

2) That resistance means that whenever electricity flows through them, they **heat up**, and some of the electrical energy is **wasted** as heat.

3) But if you **cool** some materials down to below a 'transition temperature', their **resistivity disappears entirely** and they become a **superconductor**.

4) Without any resistance, **none** of the electrical energy is turned into heat, so **none** of it's wasted. That means you can start a current flowing in a circuit using a magnetic field, take away the magnet and the current would carry on flowing **forever**... into the sunset.

5) There's a catch, though. Most 'normal' conductors, e.g. metals, have transition temperatures below **10 kelvin** (**–263 °C**). Getting things that cold is **hard**, and **really expensive**.

I couldn't find a conductor, so you'll have to make do with this instead.

6) Solid-state physicists all over the world are trying to develop **room-temperature superconductors**. So far, they've managed to get some weird **metal oxide** things to superconduct at about **140 K** (**–133 °C**), which is a much easier temperature to get down to. They've still got a long way to go though.

Uses of Superconductors

Using superconducting wires you could make:

1) **Power cables** that transmit electricity without any **loss** of power.

2) Really **strong electromagnets** that **don't** need a constant power source (for use in medical applications and Maglev trains).

3) **Electronic circuits** that work really **fast**, because there's no resistance to slow them down.

Practice Questions

Q1 Name one environmental factor likely to alter the resistance of a component.

Q2 What is special about an ohmic conductor?

Q3 What happens to a superconductor at its transition temperature?

Q4 What three factors does the resistance of a length of wire depend on?

Q5 What are the units for resistivity?

Exam Questions

Q1 Aluminium has a resistivity of 2.8×10^{-8} Ωm at 20 °C and a transition temperature of 1.2 K.

(a) Calculate the resistance of a pure aluminium wire of length 4 m and diameter 1 mm, at 20 °C.   [3 marks]

(b) The wire is cooled to a temperature of 1 K. What is its resistance now? Explain your answer.   [2 marks]

Q2 The table below shows some measurements taken by a student during an experiment investigating an unknown electrical component.

Potential Difference (V)	Current (mA)
2.0	2.67
7.0	9.33
11.0	14.67

(a) Use the first row of the table to calculate the resistance of the component when a p.d. of 2 V is applied.   [2 marks]

(b) By means of further calculation, or otherwise, decide whether the component is an ohmic conductor.   [3 marks]

Superconductors and Johnny Depp — both too cool to resist...

Superconducting electromagnets are used in magnetic resonance image (MRI) scanners in hospitals. That way, the huge magnetic fields they need can be generated without using up a load of electricity. Great stuff...

I/V Characteristics

These pages are for AQA A Unit 1, Edexcel Unit 2, OCR A Unit 2 and OCR B Unit 1.

Woohoo — real physics. This stuff's actually kind of interesting.

I/V Graphs Show how Resistance Varies

The term '**I/V characteristic**' refers to a **graph** which shows how the **current** (**I**) flowing through a **component changes** as the **potential difference** (**V**) across it is increased.

The **shallower** the **gradient** of a characteristic **I/V** graph, the **greater** the **resistance** of the component.

A **curve** shows that the resistance is **changing**.

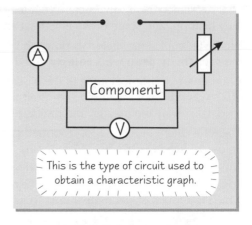

This is the type of circuit used to obtain a characteristic graph.

The I/V Characteristic for a Metallic Conductor is a Straight Line

At **constant temperature**, the **current** through a **metallic conductor** is **directly proportional** to the **voltage**. The fact that the characteristic graph is a **straight line** tells you that the **resistance doesn't change**. **Metallic conductors** are **ohmic** — they have **constant resistance provided** their temperature doesn't change.

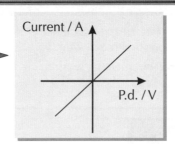

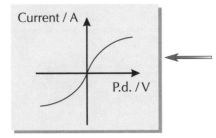

The characteristic graph for a **filament lamp** is a **curve**, which starts **steep** but gets **shallower** as the **voltage rises**. The **filament** in a lamp is just a **coiled up** length of **metal wire**, so you might think it should have the **same characteristic graph** as a **metallic conductor**. It doesn't because it **gets hot**. **Current** flowing through the lamp **increases** its **temperature**.

The **resistance of a metal increases** as the **temperature increases**.

The Temperature Affects the Charge Carriers   *Edexcel only*

1) **Charge** is carried through **metals** by **free electrons** in a **lattice** of **positive ions**.
2) Heating up a metal hardly affects how many electrons there are, but it does make it **harder** for them to **move about**. The **ions vibrate more** when heated, so the electrons **collide** with them more often, **losing energy**.

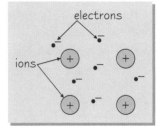

The **resistance** of most metallic conductors **goes up linearly** with **temperature**.

Semiconductors are Used in Sensors

Semiconductors are **nowhere near** as good at **conducting** electricity as **metals**. This is because there are far, far **fewer charge carriers** available. However, if **energy** is supplied to the semiconductor, **more charge carriers** are often **released**. This means that they make **excellent sensors** for detecting **changes** in their **environment**.

You need to know about **three** semiconductor components — **thermistors**, **LDRs** and **diodes**.

I/V Characteristics

The **Resistance** of a **Thermistor** Depends on **Temperature**

Thermistor circuit symbol:

A **thermistor** is a **resistor** with a **resistance** that depends on its **temperature**. You only need to know about **NTC** thermistors — NTC stands for 'Negative Temperature Coefficient'. This means that the **resistance** **decreases** as the **temperature goes up**. The characteristic graph for an NTC thermistor curves upwards.

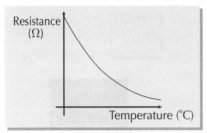

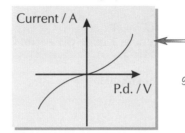

Increasing the current through the thermistor increases its temperature. The increasing gradient of this characteristic graph tells you that the resistance is decreasing.

Warming the thermistor gives more **electrons** enough **energy** to **escape** from their atoms. This means that there are **more charge carriers** available, so the resistance is lower.

The Resistance of an **LDR** depends on **Light Intensity**

LDR circuit symbol:

LDR stands for **Light-Dependent Resistor**. The **greater** the intensity of **light** shining on an LDR, the **lower** its **resistance**.

The explanation for this is similar to that for the thermistor. In this case, **light** provides the **energy** that releases more electrons. More charge carriers means a lower resistance.

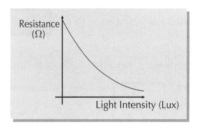

Large Dayglow Rabbit

Diodes Only Let **Current Flow** in **One Direction**

Diode and LED circuit symbols:

diode   LED

Diodes (including light emitting diodes (LEDs)) are designed to let **current flow** in **one direction** only. You don't need to be able to explain how they work, just what they do.

1)   **Forward bias** is the **direction** in which the **current** is **allowed to flow**.

2)   **Most** diodes require a **threshold voltage** of about **0.6 V** in the **forward direction** before they will conduct.

3)   In **reverse bias**, the **resistance** of the diode is **very high** and the current that flows is **very tiny**.

Practice Questions

Q1   Sketch the circuit used to determine the *I/V* characteristics of a component.

Q2   Draw an *I/V* characteristic graph for a diode.

Q3   What is an LDR?

Q4   If an *I/V* graph is curved, what does this tell you about the resistance?

Exam Question

Q1   (a) Sketch a characteristic *I/V* graph for a filament lamp.   [1 mark]

     (b) State how the resistance changes as the temperature increases.   [1 mark]

     (c) Explain why this happens.   [2 marks]

Thermistor man — temperature-dependent Mr Man...

Learn the graphs on this page, and make sure you can explain them. Whether it's a light-dependent resistor or a thermistor, the same principle applies. More energy releases more charge carriers, and more charge carriers means a lower resistance.

Electrical Energy, Power and Fuses

These pages are for AQA A Unit 1, Edexcel Unit 2, OCR A Unit 2 and OCR B Unit 1.

Power and energy are pretty familiar concepts — and here they are again. Same principles, just different equations.

Power is the Rate of Transfer of Energy

Power (P) is **defined** as the **rate** of **transfer** of **energy**.
It's measured in **watts (W)**, where **1 watt** is equivalent to **1 joule per second**.

or $P = \dfrac{E}{t}$

There's a really simple formula for **power** in **electrical circuits**:

$$P = VI$$

This makes sense, since:

1) **Potential difference (V)** is defined as the **energy transferred** per **coulomb**.
2) **Current (I)** is defined as the **number** of **coulombs** transferred per **second**.
3) So **p.d.** × **current** is **energy transferred per second**, i.e. **power**.

You know from the definition of **resistance** that: $\boxed{V = IR}$

Clive was desperate to be an orange power ranger

Combining the **two equations** gives you loads of **different ways** to **calculate power**.

$$P = VI \qquad P = \dfrac{V^2}{R} \qquad P = I^2R$$

Obviously, which equation you should use depends on what **quantities** you're given in the **question**.

Energy is Easy to Calculate if you Know the Power

Sometimes it's the **total energy** transferred that you're interested in. In this case you simply need to **multiply** the **power** by the **time**. So:

$$E = VIt \qquad \text{(or } E = \dfrac{V^2}{R}t \quad \text{or } E = I^2Rt\text{)}$$

You've got to make sure that the time is in seconds.

The rest of this stuff (the kWh and fuses) is just for OCR A Unit 2. The rest of you can go straight to the questions.

Electricity Companies don't use Joules and Watts

Electricity companies charge their customers for '**units**' of electricity. Another name for a unit is a **kilowatt-hour (kWh)**. If you know the **power** of an **appliance** and the **length of time** it's used for you can work out the **energy** it uses in kWh.

Energy	=	Power	×	Time
(kWh)		(kW)		(h)

1 kW = 1000 W
1 hour = 60 minutes = 3600 seconds

1 kWh = 3.6 million joules

The **joule** is the **SI** unit of **energy**, but a joule is such a **small amount** of energy compared with the amount a typical household uses every month that it's **impractical**.

Example

A **1500 W** hairdryer is on for **10 minutes**. How much energy does it use in J and kWh?

$E = Pt = 1500 \times 10 \times 60 = \boxed{900\ 000\ \text{J}}$ $E = Pt = 1.5 \times 1/6 = \boxed{0.25\ \text{kWh}}$

Electrical Energy, Power and Fuses

Fuses Prevent Shocks and Fire   OCR A only

A **fuse** is a very **fine wire** in a glass tube that's connected between the **live terminal** of the mains supply and an **appliance**. If the **current** in the circuit gets too **big** (bigger than the fuse rating — see below), the fuse wire **melts** and **breaks** the circuit. Fuses should be rated as near as possible but **just higher** than the normal operating current.

The **earth wire** and **fuse** in an appliance with a metal case work together like this:

1) The earth pin in the plug is connected to the **case** of the appliance via the **earth wire**.

2) A **fault** can develop in which the **live** somehow **touches** the case. Then because the case is earthed, a big current flows **in** through the **live**, through the **case** and **out** down the **earth** wire.

3) This **surge** in current blows the fuse, which cuts off the live supply. This prevents electric shocks from the case.

You Can Work Out What Fuse to Use from the Appliance's Power Rating

Most electrical goods have a plate showing their **power rating** and **voltage rating**.
To work out the fuse needed, you have to work out the current that the appliance will normally draw.

Example   A toaster is rated at 2.2 kW, 230 V. Find the fuse needed.   *You can usually only get fuses with ratings of 3 A, 5 A or 13 A.*

Use $P = VI$, and rearrange to give $I = P / V = 2200 / 230 = \textbf{9.57 A}$.
The fuse should be rated just a bit higher than the normal current, so this toaster should have a 13 A fuse.

Practice Questions

Q1   Write down the equation linking power, current and resistance.
Q2   How many joules is 1 kWh?
Q3   Power is measured in watts. What is 1 watt equivalent to?

Exam Questions

Q1   This question concerns a mains powered hairdryer, the circuit diagram for which is given below.

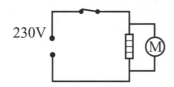

(a) The heater has a power of 920 W in normal operation. Calculate the current in the heater.   [2 marks]

(b) The motor has a resistance of 190 Ω.
    What current will flow through the motor when the hairdryer is switched on?   [2 marks]

(c) Show that the total power of the hairdryer in normal operation is just under 1.2 kW.   [2 marks]

(d) Calculate the number of kilowatt-hours of electrical energy converted if the hairdryer
    is used for 15 minutes.   [1 mark]

Q2   A 12 V car battery supplies a current of 48 A for 2 seconds to the car's starter motor.
    The total resistance of the connecting wires is 0.01 Ω.

(a) Calculate the energy transferred from the battery.   [1 mark]

(b) Calculate the energy wasted as heat in the wires.   [2 marks]

Hurrah — now my toaster won't kill me...

Whenever you get equations in this book, you know you're gonna have to learn them. Fact of life.
I used to find it helped to stick big lists of equations all over my walls in the run up to the exams. But as that's
possibly the least cool wallpaper imaginable, I don't advise inviting your friends round till after the exams...

E.m.f. and Internal Resistance

These pages are for AQA A Unit 1, Edexcel Unit 2, OCR A Unit 2 and OCR B Unit 1.

There's resistance everywhere — inside batteries, in all the wires and in the components themselves.
No one's for giving current an easy ride.

From now on, I'm assuming that the resistance of the wires in the circuit is zero. In practice, they do have a small resistance.

Batteries have Resistance

Resistance comes from **electrons colliding** with **atoms** and **losing energy**.

In a **battery**, **chemical energy** is used to make **electrons move**. As they move, they collide with atoms inside the battery — so batteries **must** have resistance. This is called **internal resistance**.

Internal resistance is what makes **batteries** and **cells warm up** when they're used.

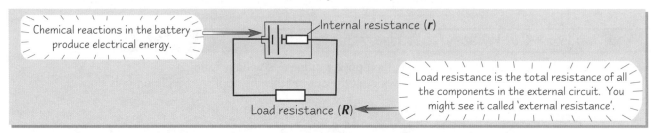

Chemical reactions in the battery produce electrical energy.

Internal resistance (*r*)

Load resistance is the total resistance of all the components in the external circuit. You might see it called 'external resistance'.

Load resistance (*R*)

1) The amount of **electrical energy** the battery produces for each **coulomb** of charge is called its **electromotive force** or **e.m.f.** (ε). Be careful — e.m.f. **isn't** actually a force. It's measured in **volts**.

2) The **potential difference** across the **load resistance** (*R*) is the **energy transferred** when **one coulomb** of charge flows through the **load resistance**. This potential difference is called the **terminal p.d.** (*V*).

3) If there was **no internal resistance**, the **terminal p.d.** would be the **same** as the **e.m.f.** However, in **real** power supplies, there's **always some energy lost** overcoming the internal resistance.

4) The **energy wasted per coulomb** overcoming the internal resistance is called the **lost volts** (*v*).

Conservation of energy tells us:

energy per coulomb supplied by the source	=	energy per coulomb used in load resistance	+	energy per coulomb wasted in internal resistance

There are Loads of Calculations with E.m.f. and Internal Resistance

Examiners can ask you to do **calculations** with **e.m.f.** and **internal resistance** in loads of **different** ways. You've got to be ready for whatever they throw at you.

$$\varepsilon = V + v \qquad \varepsilon = I\,(R + r)$$
$$V = \varepsilon - v \qquad V = \varepsilon - Ir$$

Learn these equations for the exam. Only one of them will be on your formula sheet.

These are all basically the **same equation**, just written differently. If you're given enough information you can calculate the e.m.f. (ε), terminal p.d. (*V*), lost volts (*v*), current (*I*), load resistance (*R*) or internal resistance (*r*). Which equation you should use depends on what information you've got, and what you need to calculate.

Most Power Supplies Need Low Internal Resistance

A **car battery** has to deliver a **really high current** — so it needs to have a **low internal resistance**. The cells used to power a **torch** or a **personal stereo** are the **same**. **Generally**, batteries have an **internal resistance** of **less than 1Ω**.

Since **internal resistance** causes **energy loss**, you'd think **all** power supplies should have a **low internal resistance**.

High voltage power supplies are the **exception**. **HT** (high tension) and **EHT** (extremely high tension) **supplies** are designed with **very high** internal resistances. This means that if they're **accidentally short-circuited** only a **very small current** can flow. Much **safer**.

E.m.f. and Internal Resistance

Use this **Circuit** to **Measure Internal Resistance** and **E.m.f.**

By **changing** the value of **R** (**load resistance**) in this circuit and **measuring** the **current** (**I**) and **p.d.** (**V**), you can work out the **internal resistance** of the source.

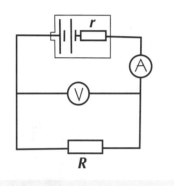

Start with the equation:

$$V = \mathcal{E} - Ir$$

Plot a graph of **V** against **I**.

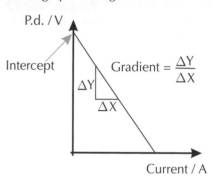

1) Rearrange the equation: $V = -rI + \mathcal{E}$
2) Since **E** and **r** are constants, that's just the equation of a **straight line** (in the form: $y = mx + c$).
3) So the intercept on the vertical axis is $\mathcal{E}$.
4) And the gradient is **–r**.

Equation of a straight line
$$y = \mathbf{mx} + \mathbf{c}$$
gradient   y-intercept

An **easier** way to **measure** the **e.m.f.** of a **power source** is by connecting a high-resistance **voltmeter** across its **terminals**. A **small current flows** through the **voltmeter**, so there must be some **lost volts** — this means you measure a value **very slightly less** than the **e.m.f.** In **practice** the difference **isn't** usually **significant**.

Practice Questions

Q1 What causes internal resistance?

Q2 What is meant by 'lost volts'?

Q3 What is the difference between e.m.f. and terminal p.d.?

Q4 Write the equation used to calculate the terminal p.d. of a power supply.

Exam Questions

Q1 A large battery with an internal resistance of 0.8 Ω and e.m.f. 24 V is used to power a dentist's drill with resistance 4 Ω.

(a) Calculate the current in the circuit when the drill is connected to the power supply. [2 marks]

(b) Calculate the voltage across the drill while it is being used. [1 mark]

Q2 A student mistakenly connects a 10 Ω ray box to an HT power supply of 500 V. The ray box does not light, and the student measures the current flowing to be only 50 mA.

(a) Calculate the internal resistance of the HT power supply. [2 marks]

(b) Explain why this is a sensible internal resistance for an HT power supply. [2 marks]

You're UNBELIEVABLE... [Frantic air guitar]... Ueuuurrrghhh... Yeah...

Wanting power supplies to have a low internal resistance makes sense, you wouldn't want your MP3 player battery melting if you listened to music for more than half an hour. Make sure you know your e.m.f. equations, they're an exam fave. A good way to get them learnt is to keep trying to getting from one equation to another... dull, but it can help.

Conservation of Energy & Charge in Circuits

These pages are for AQA A Unit 1, Edexcel Unit 2, OCR A Unit 2 and OCR B Unit 1.

There are some things in Physics that are so fundamental that you just have to accept them. Like the fact that there's loads of Maths in it. And that energy is conserved. And that Physicists get more homework than everyone else.

Charge Doesn't 'Leak Away' Anywhere — it's Conserved

1) As **charge flows** through a circuit, it **doesn't** get **used up** or **lost**.

2) This means that whatever **charge flows into** a junction will **flow out** again.

3) Since **current** is **rate of flow of charge**, it follows that whatever **current flows into** a junction is the same as the current **flowing out** of it.

e.g.
CHARGE FLOWING IN 1 SECOND
$Q_1 = 6\,C \Rightarrow I_1 = 6\,A$ $\longrightarrow$ $Q_2 = 2\,C \Rightarrow I_2 = 2\,A$
$Q_3 = 4\,C \Rightarrow I_3 = 4\,A$
$I_1 = I_2 + I_3$

Kirchhoff's first law says:

> The total **current entering a junction** = the total **current leaving it.**

Energy conservation is vital.

Energy is Conserved too

1) **Energy is conserved**. You already know that. In **electrical circuits**, **energy** is **transferred round** the circuit. Energy **transferred to** a charge is **e.m.f.**, and energy **transferred from** a charge is **potential difference**.

2) In a **closed loop**, these two quantities must be **equal** if energy is conserved (which it is).

Kirchhoff's second law says:

> The **total e.m.f.** around a **series circuit** = the **sum** of the **p.d.s** across each component. (or $\varepsilon = \Sigma IR$ in symbols)

Exam Questions get you to Apply Kirchhoff's Laws to Combinations of Resistors

A **typical exam question** will give you a **circuit** with bits of information missing, leaving you to fill in the gaps. Not the most fun... but on the plus side you get to ignore any internal resistance stuff (unless the question tells you otherwise)... hurrah. You need to remember the **following rules:**

SERIES Circuits

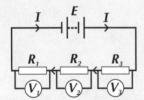

1) **same current** at **all points** of the circuit (since there are no junctions)

2) **e.m.f. split** between **components** (by Kirchhoff's 2nd law), so:
$E = V_1 + V_2 + V_3$

3) $V = IR$, so if I is constant:
$IR_{total} = IR_1 + IR_2 + IR_3$

4) cancelling the Is gives:

$$R_{total} = R_1 + R_2 + R_3$$

PARALLEL Circuits

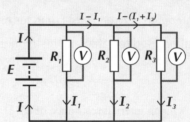

1) **current** is **split** at each **junction**, so:
$I = I_1 + I_2 + I_3$

2) **same p.d.** across **all components** (three separate loops — within each loop the e.m.f. equals sum of individual p.d.s)

3) so, $V/R_{total} = V/R_1 + V/R_2 + V/R_3$

4) cancelling the Vs gives:

$$1/R_{total} = 1/R_1 + 1/R_2 + 1/R_3$$

Or in terms of **conductance** (for *OCR B*):

$$G = G_1 + G_2 + G_3$$

...and there's an example on the next page to make sure you know what to do with all that...

Conservation of Energy & Charge in Circuits

Worked Exam Question

A battery of e.m.f. 16 V and negligible internal resistance is connected in a circuit as shown:

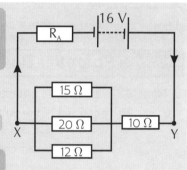

a) Show that the group of resistors between X and Y could be replaced by a single resistor of resistance 15 Ω.

You can find the **combined resistance** of the 15 Ω, 20 Ω and 12 Ω resistors using:

$1/R = 1/R_1 + 1/R_2 + 1/R_3 = 1/15 + 1/20 + 1/12 = 1/5 \quad \Rightarrow R = 5\ \Omega$

So **overall resistance** between **X** and **Y** can be found by $R = R_1 + R_2 = 5 + 10 = \mathbf{15\ \Omega}$

b) If $R_A = 20\ \Omega$:
  (i) calculate the potential difference across R_A,

Careful — there are a few steps here. You need the p.d. across R_A, but you don't know the current through it. So start there:

total resistance in circuit = 20 + 15 = 35 Ω, **so** current through R_A can be found using $I = V_{total}/R_{total}$:

$I = 16/35\ A$

then you can use $V = IR_A$ to find the p.d. across R_A: $\boxed{V = 16/35 \times 20 = \mathbf{9.1\ V}}$

  (ii) calculate the current in the 15 Ω resistor.

You know the **current flowing** into the group of three resistors and out of it, but not through the individual branches. But you know that their **combined resistance** is **5 Ω** (from part a) so you can work out the p.d. across the group:

$V = IR = 16/35 \times 5 = 16/7\ V$

The p.d. across the **whole group** is the same as the p.d. across each **individual resistor**, so you can use this to find the current through the 15 Ω resistor:

$\boxed{I = V/R = (16/7) / 15 = \mathbf{0.15\ A}}$

Practice Questions

Q1 State Kirchhoff's laws.

Q2 Find the current through and potential difference across each of two 5 Ω resistors when they are placed in a circuit containing a 5V battery, and are wired: a) in series, b) in parallel.

Exam Question

Q1 For the circuit on the right:

  (a) Calculate the total effective resistance of the three resistors in this combination.   [2 marks]

  (b) Calculate the main current, I_3.   [2 marks]

  (c) Calculate the potential difference across the 4 Ω resistor.   [1 mark]

  (d) Calculate the potential difference across the parallel pair of resistors.
                                    [1 mark]

  (e) Using your answer from 1 (d), calculate the currents I_1 and I_2.   [2 marks]

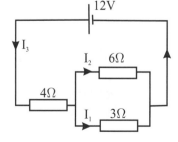

This is a very purple page — needs a bit of yellow I think...

V = IR is the formula you'll use most often in these questions. Make sure you know whether you're using it on the overall circuit, or just one specific component. It's amazingly easy to get muddled up — you've been warned.

The Potential Divider

These pages are for AQA A Unit 1, Edexcel Unit 2, OCR A Unit 2 and OCR B Unit 1.

I remember the days when potential dividers were pretty much the hardest thing they could throw at you. Then along came AS Physics. Hey ho.

Anyway, in context this doesn't seem too hard now, so get stuck in.

Use a **Potential Divider** to get a **Fraction** of a **Source Voltage**

1) At its simplest, a **potential divider** is a circuit with a **voltage source** and a couple of **resistors** in series.

2) The **potential** of the voltage source (e.g. a power supply) is **divided** in the **ratio** of the **resistances**. So, if you had a **2 Ω** resistor and a **3 Ω** resistor, you'd get **2/5** of the p.d. across the **2 Ω** resistor and **3/5** across the **3 Ω**.

3) That means you can **choose** the **resistances** to get the **voltage** you **want** across one of them.

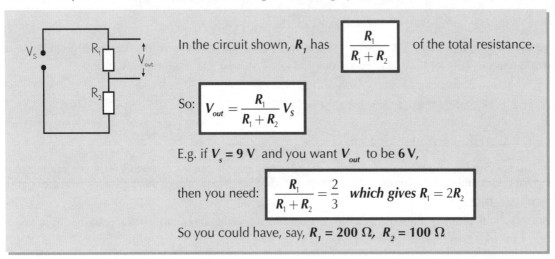

In the circuit shown, R_1 has $\dfrac{R_1}{R_1 + R_2}$ of the total resistance.

So: $$V_{out} = \frac{R_1}{R_1 + R_2} V_s$$

E.g. if $V_s = 9\,V$ and you want V_{out} to be **6 V**,

then you need: $\dfrac{R_1}{R_1 + R_2} = \dfrac{2}{3}$ *which gives* $R_1 = 2R_2$

So you could have, say, $R_1 = 200\,\Omega$, $R_2 = 100\,\Omega$

4) This circuit is mainly used for **calibrating voltmeters**, which have a **very high resistance**.

5) If you put something with a **relatively low resistance** across R_1 though, you start to run into **problems**. You've **effectively** got **two resistors** in **parallel**, which will **always** have a **total** resistance **less** than R_1. That means that V_{out} will be **less** than you've calculated, and will depend on what's connected across R_1. Hrrumph.

Add an **LDR** or **Thermistor** for a **Light** or **Temperature Switch**

1) A **light-dependent resistor** (LDR) has a very **high resistance** in the **dark**, but a **lower resistance** in the **light**.

2) An **NTC thermistor** has a **high resistance** at **low temperatures**, but a much **lower resistance** at **high temperatures** (it varies in the opposite way to a normal resistor, only much more so).

3) Either of these can be used as one of the **resistors** in a **potential divider**, giving an **output voltage** that **varies** with the **light level** or **temperature**.

4) Add a **transistor** and you've got yourself a **switch**, e.g. to turn on a light or a heating system.

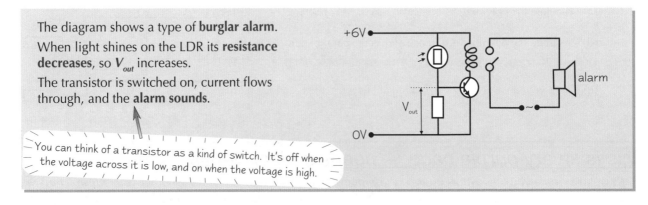

The diagram shows a type of **burglar alarm**.
When light shines on the LDR its **resistance decreases**, so V_{out} increases.
The transistor is switched on, current flows through, and the **alarm sounds**.

You can think of a transistor as a kind of switch. It's off when the voltage across it is low, and on when the voltage is high.

The Potential Divider

A *Potentiometer* uses a *Variable Resistor* to give a *Variable Voltage*

1) A **potentiometer** has a variable resistor replacing R_1 and R_2 of the potential divider, but it uses the **same idea** (it's even sometimes **called** a potential divider just to confuse things).

2) You move a **slider** or turn a knob to **adjust** the **relative sizes** of R_1 and R_2. That way you can vary V_{out} from **0 V** up to the source voltage.

3) This is dead handy when you want to be able to **change** a **voltage continuously**, like in the **volume control** of a stereo.

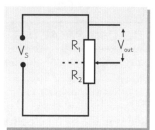

Here, V_s is replaced by the input signal (e.g. from a CD player) and V_{out} is the output to the amplifier and loudspeaker.

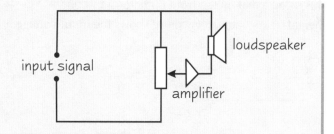

Practice Questions

Q1 Look at the burglar alarm circuit on page 58. How could you change the circuit so that the alarm sounds when the light level decreases?

Q2 The LDR in the burglar alarm circuit has a resistance of 300 Ω when light and 900 Ω when dark. The fixed resistor has a value of 100 Ω. Show that V_{out} (light) = 1.5 V and V_{out} (dark) = 0.6 V.

Exam Questions

Q1 In the circuit on the right, all the resistors have the same value. Calculate the p.d. between:

    (i)   A and B.   [1 mark]

    (ii)   A and C.   [1 mark]

    (iii) B and C.   [1 mark]

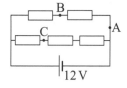

Q2 Look at the circuit on the right.

    (a)   Calculate the p.d. between A and B as shown by a high resistance voltmeter placed between the two points.   [1 mark]

    (b)   A 40 Ω resistor is now placed between points A and B. Calculate the p.d. across AB and the current flowing through the 40 Ω resistor.   [4 marks]

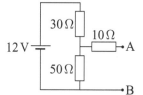

OI...YOU... [bang bang bang]... turn that potentiometer down...

You'll probably have to use a potentiometer in every experiment you do with electricity from now on in, so you'd better get used to them. I can't stand the things myself, but then lab and me don't mix — far too technical.

Alternating Current

These pages are for AQA A Unit 1 only.

Just when you think you've got the hang of this electricity lark, they spring alternating current on you. Here's where it all gets way more complicated. You can't use a normal voltmeter and ammeter any more — enter 'the oscilloscope'.

An **Oscilloscope** can show the **Waveform** of an **Alternating Current**

An **alternating** current or voltage is one that **changes with time**. The voltage goes up and down in a **regular pattern** — some of the time it's **positive** and some of the time it's **negative**.

1) An **oscilloscope** is basically a snazzy **voltmeter**.

2) The **trace** you see is made by an **electron beam** moving across a screen.

3) The **time base** controls how **fast** the beam is moved across the screen. You can **set** this using a **dial** on the **front** of the oscilloscope.

4) The **vertical height** of the trace at any point shows the **input voltage** at that point.

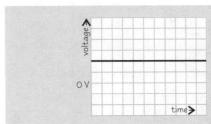

A **direct current** (d.c.) source is always at the same voltage, so you get a **horizontal line**.

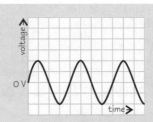

An **alternating current** (a.c.) source gives a regularly **repeating waveform**.

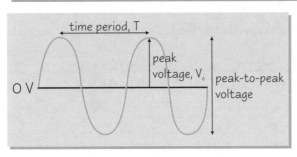

Measuring the **distance** between successive **peaks** along the time axis gives you the **time period** (as long as you know the time base setting).

You can use this to calculate the **frequency**:

$$frequency = \frac{1}{time\ period} \qquad f = \frac{1}{T}$$

This is the same for any type of wave.

The **peak voltage** is useful to know, though it's often **easier** to measure the **peak-to-peak voltage** and **halve** it.

V_{rms} and I_{rms} are often the **best ways** to Describe an **Alternating Current**

1) An **a.c. supply** with a **peak voltage** of **2 V** will be **below 2 V** most of the time. That means it won't have as high a power output as a **2 V d.c. supply**.

2) To **compare** them properly, you need to **average** the **a.c. voltage** somehow.

3) A **normal average won't work**, because the **positive** and **negative** bits **cancel out**. It turns out that something called the **root mean square (r.m.s.) voltage** does the trick.

4) For a **sine wave**, you get this by **dividing** the **peak voltage**, V_o, by $\sqrt{2}$. And it's the **same** for the **current**:

$$V_{rms} = \frac{V_o}{\sqrt{2}} \qquad\qquad I_{rms} = \frac{I_o}{\sqrt{2}}$$

Even though this is only strictly true if the a.c. signal is a sine wave, that's what you get from a generator. It's also the only one on your syllabus, so I wouldn't worry about it.

5) If you want to work out the **power**, just replace I and V in the power formula with the **r.m.s. values**.

$$Power = V_{rms} \times I_{rms}$$

Alternating Current

For the **resistance** it doesn't matter, as the **peak values** will give you the same answer:

$$Resistance,\ R = \frac{V_{rms}}{I_{rms}} = \frac{V_o}{I_o}$$

It's usually the **r.m.s. value** that's stated on a **power supply**.

For example, the value of **230 V** stated for the **UK mains electricity supply** is the **r.m.s. value**.
Just use the equation above to get the **peak** value, or double that to get the **peak-to-peak** value:

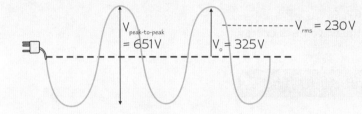

$V_{peak-to-peak}$ = 651V V_o = 325V V_{rms} = 230V

$$V_{peak} = \sqrt{2} \times V_{rms} = 325\ \mathbf{V}$$

$$V_{peak\text{-}to\text{-}peak} = 2 \times V_{peak} = 651\ \mathbf{V}$$

Practice Questions

Q1 Define the terms 'time period' and 'frequency' for an alternating signal.

Q2 Define the r.m.s. voltage of an alternating sinusoidal signal in terms of the peak voltage.

Q3 Why are the r.m.s. values for current and voltage used to work out the power of a.c. supplies rather than the peak values?

Exam Questions

Q1 A CRO is used to study the waveform of a sinusoidal alternating voltage of frequency 100 Hz and peak voltage of 2.0 V. The time base is set to 2.0 ms cm^{-1} horizontally and the voltage sensitivity vertically is 0.5 Vcm^{-1}.

Draw the trace you expect on a 10 cm square grid and show all your working.   [4 marks]

Q2 An oscilloscope is set up initially with a horizontal line at zero volts, and the time base set to 5.0 ms per division. The Y-input voltage sensitivity is set at 1.0 volt per division.

Sketch the traces you would expect if each of the following were connected to the oscilloscope.

(a) A 2.0 V cell.   [2 marks]

(b) An a.c. signal of 1.5 V peak value and frequency 50 Hz.   [3 marks]

Q3 Five cycles of a.c. are observed on a CRO screen marked with 10 divisions horizontally and vertically. The frequency of the signal is 2500 Hz.

Work out:

(a) The time period of the signal.   [1 mark]

(b) The horizontal time-base in both seconds per division and ms per division.   [2 marks]

Yay, oscilloscopes — cool...

This stuff on a.c. electricity isn't too complicated — you just need to make sure you know all the equations on these two pages. Remember, any current or voltage you read off an a.c. power supply will be r.m.s.

The Nature of Waves

These pages are for AQA A Unit 2, Edexcel Unit 2, OCR A Unit 2 and OCR B Unit 1.

Aaaah... playing with slinky springs and waggling ropes about. It's all good clean fun as my mate Richard used to say...

A **Wave Transfers Energy** Away from Its Source

A **progressive** (moving) wave carries **energy** from one place to another **without transferring any material**.
Here are some ways you can tell waves carry energy:

1) Electromagnetic waves cause things to **heat up**.
2) **X-rays** and **gamma rays** knock electrons out of their orbits, causing **ionisation**.
3) Loud **sounds** make things **vibrate**.
4) **Wave power** can be used to **generate electricity**.
5) Since waves carry energy away, the **source** of the wave **loses energy**.

Here are all the **bits** of a **Wave** you Need to Know

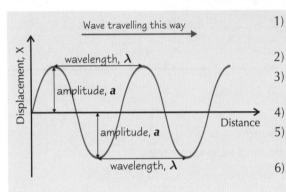

1) **Displacement, X, metres** — how far a **point** on the wave has **moved** from its **undisturbed position**.
2) **Amplitude, a, metres** — **maximum displacement**.
3) **Wavelength, λ, metres** — the **length** of **one whole wave**, from **crest** to **crest** or **trough** to **trough**.
4) **Period, T, seconds** — the **time taken** for a **whole vibration**.
5) **Frequency, f, hertz** — the **number** of **vibrations per second** passing a given **point**.
6) **Phase difference** — the amount by which **one wave lags behind another** wave. **Measured** in **degrees** or **radians**. See page 80.

Waves Can Be **Reflected** and **Refracted**

Reflection — the wave is **bounced back** when it **hits a boundary**. E.g. you can see the reflection of light in mirrors. The reflection of water waves can be demonstrated in a ripple tank.

Refraction — the wave **changes direction** as it enters a **different medium**. The change in direction is a result of the wave slowing down or speeding up (see page 76).

Intensity is a Measure of **How Much Energy** a Wave is Carrying

1) When you talk about "**brightness**" for light or "**loudness**" for sound, what you really mean is **how much light** or **sound** energy hits your eyes or your ears **per second**.
2) The scientific measure of this is **intensity** (or **radiation flux** for light at a surface).

> Intensity is the **rate of flow** of energy per **unit area** at **right angles** to the **direction of travel** of the wave. It's measured in **Wm⁻²**.

Intensity is **Proportional** to the **Square** of the **Amplitude** of the **Wave**

$$I \propto A^2$$

1) This comes from the fact that intensity is proportional to energy, and the energy of a wave depends on the square of the amplitude.
2) From this you can tell that for a vibrating source it takes four times as much energy to double the size of the vibrations.

The Nature of Waves

The **Frequency** is the **Inverse** of the **Period**

$$Frequency = \frac{1}{period}$$

It's that simple.
Get the **units** straight: **1 Hz = 1 s⁻¹**.

Wave **Speed**, **Frequency** and **Wavelength** are Linked by the **Wave Equation**

Wave speed can be measured just like the speed of anything else:

$$Speed\ (v) = \frac{distance\ moved\ (d)}{time\ taken\ (t)}$$

Remember, you're not measuring how fast a physical point (like one molecule of rope) moves. You're measuring how fast a point on the **wave pattern** moves.

Learn the **Wave Equation**...

$$Speed\ of\ wave\ (v) = wavelength\ (\lambda) \times frequency\ (f)$$

$$v = \lambda f$$

You need to be able to rearrange this equation for v, λ or f.

... and How to **Derive** it

You can work out the **wave equation** by imagining **how long** it takes for the **crest** of a wave to **move** across a **distance** of **one wavelength**. The **distance travelled** is **λ**. **By definition**, the **time taken** to travel **one whole wavelength** is the **period** of the wave, which is equal to **1/f**.

$$Speed\ (v) = \frac{distance\ moved\ (d)}{time\ taken\ (t)} \longrightarrow Speed\ (v) = \frac{distance\ moved\ (\lambda)}{time\ taken\ (1/f)}$$

Learn to recognise when to use **v = λf** and when to use **v = d/t**. Look at which variables are mentioned in the question.

Practice Questions

Q1 Does a wave carry matter **or** energy from one place to another?

Q2 Diffraction and interference are two wave properties. Write down two more.

Q3 Write down the relationship between the amplitude of a wave and its intensity.

Q4 Give the units of frequency, displacement and amplitude.

Q5 Write down the equation connecting **v**, **λ** and **f**.

Exam Question

Q1 A buoy floating on the sea takes 6 seconds to rise and fall once (complete a full period of oscillation). The difference in height between the buoy at its lowest and highest points is 1.2 m, and waves pass it at a speed of 3 ms⁻¹.

(a) How long are the waves? [2 marks]

(b) What is the amplitude of the waves? [1 mark]

Learn the wave equation and its derivation — pure poetry...

This isn't too difficult to start you off — most of it you'll have done at GCSE anyway. But once again, it's a whole bunch of equations to learn, and you won't get far without learning them. Yada yada.

Longitudinal and Transverse Waves

These pages are for AQA A Unit 2, Edexcel Unit 2, OCR A Unit 2 and OCR B Unit 1.

There are different types of wave — and the difference is easiest to see using a slinky. Try it — you'll have hours of fun.

In **Transverse Waves** the **Vibration** is at **Right Angles** to the **Direction** of Travel

All **electromagnetic waves** are **transverse**. Other examples of transverse waves are **ripples** on water and waves on **ropes**.

There are **two** main ways of **drawing** transverse waves:

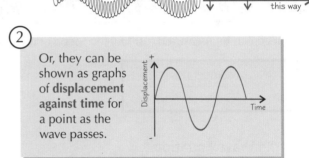

① They can be shown as **graphs** of **displacement** against **distance** along the path of the wave.

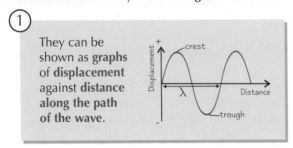

② Or, they can be shown as graphs of **displacement** against **time** for a point as the wave passes.

Both sorts of graph often give the **same shape**, so make sure you check out the label on the **x-axis**.
Displacements **upwards** from the centre line are given a **+ sign**. Displacements downwards are given a **– sign**.

In **Longitudinal Waves** the **Vibrations** are **Along** the Direction of Travel

The most **common** example of a **longitudinal wave** is **sound**. A sound wave consists of alternate **compressions** and **rarefactions** of the **medium** it's travelling through. (That's why sound can't go through a vacuum.) Some types of **earthquake shock waves** are also longitudinal.

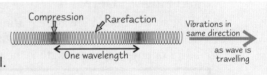

It's hard to **represent** longitudinal waves **graphically**. You'll usually see them plotted as **displacement** against **time**. These can be **confusing** though, because they look like a **transverse wave**.

A **Polarised Wave** only **Oscillates** In One Direction

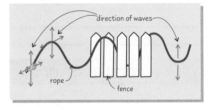

1) If you **shake a rope** to make a **wave** you can move your hand **up and down** or **side to side** or in a **mixture** of directions — it still makes a **transverse wave**.

2) But if you try to pass **waves in a rope** through a **vertical fence**, the wave will only get through if the **vibrations are vertical**. The fence filters out vibration in other directions. This is called **polarising** the wave.

3) Ordinary **light waves** are a mixture of **different directions** of **vibration**. (The things vibrating are electric and magnetic fields.) A **polarising filter** only transmits vibrations in one direction.

4) If you have two polarising filters at **right angles** to each other, then **no** light will get through.

5) Polarisation **can only happen** for **transverse** waves. The fact that you can polarise light is one **proof** that it's a transverse wave.

When **Light Reflects** it is **Partially Polarised**

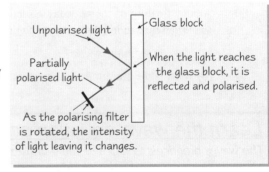

1) Rotating a **polarising filter** in a beam of light shows the fraction of the light that is vibrating in each **direction**.

2) If you direct a beam of unpolarised light at a reflective surface then view the **reflected ray** through a polarising filter, the intensity of light leaving the filter **changes** with the **orientation** of the filter.

3) The intensity changes because light is **partially polarised** when it is **reflected**.

4) This effect is used to remove **unwanted reflections** in photography and in **Polaroid sunglasses** to remove **glare**.

Longitudinal and Transverse Waves

Materials Can **Rotate** the **Plane of Polarisation** — *Edexcel only*

The **plane** in which a wave moves and **vibrates** is called the **plane of polarisation** — e.g. the rope on the last page was polarised in the **vertical** plane by the fence. Some **materials** (e.g. crystals) **rotate** the plane of polarised light. You can **measure** how much a material rotates the plane of polarised light using two **polarising filters**:

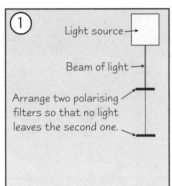

① Light source → Beam of light →

Arrange two polarising filters so that no light leaves the second one.

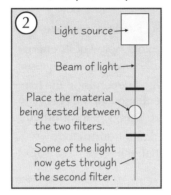

② Light source → Beam of light →

Place the material being tested between the two filters.

Some of the light now gets through the second filter.

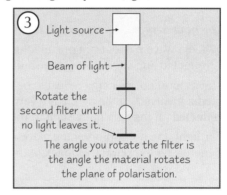

③ Light source → Beam of light →

Rotate the second filter until no light leaves it.

The angle you rotate the filter is the angle the material rotates the plane of polarisation.

Rotating the **Plane of Polarisation** Affects the **Intensity** — *OCR A only*

You've seen that passing light through a polarising filter **rotates** its **plane of polarisation**, but it also changes the **amplitude** and **intensity** of the transmitted wave.

The **amplitude** of the **transmitted** wave is the **component** of the **incident** wave in the direction of the **new plane** of polarisation.

$$A = A_0 \cos \theta$$

Where A is the amplitude of the **transmitted** wave, A_0 is the amplitude of the **incident** wave and θ (theta) is the **angle** the plane has been rotated.

The **intensity** of the **transmitted** light is **proportional** to the **amplitude squared** — this is **Malus' law**.

$$I = I_0 \cos^2 \theta$$

Where I is the intensity of transmitted light, I_0 is the intensity of incident light and θ (theta) is the **angle** the plane has been rotated.

Practice Questions

Q1 Give examples of a transverse wave and a longitudinal wave.

Q2 What is a polarised wave? How can you polarise a wave?

Q3 What is Malus' law and what is it used for?

Exam Questions

Q1 In an experiment, light is shone through a disc of a crystal called "Iceland spar". The beam of light is less bright when it emerges from the crystal than when it enters. Next, a second identical disc of Iceland spar is placed in front of the first. The first disc is held steady while the second is rotated (in the plane of the disc). The intensity of light emerging changes as the second disc rotates. At two points in each rotation, no light gets through at all.

(a) Explain the results of these experiments. You may use a diagram to help your answer. [5 marks]

(b) When the second disc is rotated to angle α, the intensity of light emerging from the second disc is half the value it was when it left the first disc. Calculate angle α. [3 marks]

Q2 Give one example of an application of polarisation and explain how it works. [2 marks]

Caution — rotating the plane may cause nausea...

The waves broadcast from TV or radio transmitters are polarised. So you have to line up the receiving aerial with the transmitting aerial to receive the signal properly. It's one reason why the TV picture's lousy if the aerial gets knocked.

Ultrasound Imaging

These pages are for Edexcel Unit 2 only.

Now that you've seen how waves work, it's time to see what they're used for — scanning, that's what.

Waves are **Reflected** and **Transmitted** at **Interfaces**

1) The **boundary** between two different media is called an **interface**.

2) When a wave passes from one medium to another, some of its **energy** is **reflected** and some of it is **transmitted** — as shown in the diagram.

3) The proportion of energy reflected or transmitted depends on the two media involved. If the media are very **different**, most of the energy is **reflected**. If they are quite **similar**, most of the energy is **transmitted**.

4) For **light**, the proportion of the wave reflected and transmitted depends on the **refractive index** of the two materials (see page 78).

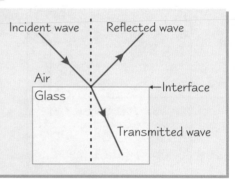

The **Reflection** of **Ultrasound Waves** is Used in **Ultrasound Scans**

1) Ultrasound scans use short pulses of **ultrasound radiation** to form images of the inside of your body.

2) The ultrasound is directed into your body using a **transducer**. If you have air between the transducer and your skin, most of the waves are **reflected** because air is a very **different** medium from skin. So a **gel** is applied to the transducer to **increase** the proportion of ultrasound waves that **enter** your body.

3) When the ultrasound waves reach an **interface** inside your body — e.g. between different types of tissue — some of them are **reflected**. A computer attached to the transducer calculates how far from the surface of your skin the interface is by **timing** how long it takes for the reflected waves to **return**.

4) The computer uses the information about the **location** of the boundaries between different tissues to build up an **image** of the inside of your body.

A similar technique is used in **sonar** — e.g. ships send sonar pulses (**ultrasound waves**) down towards the seabed and the pulses are **reflected** back from any **submerged** objects. It can also be used to measure the **speed** of objects.

You Can **Measure** the **Speed** of Objects Using the **Doppler Effect**

1) If you stand **still** and listen to the sound of the horn of a **stationary** car, you'll hear the **same pitch** sound no matter where you stand.

2) But if the car is **moving** when it sounds its horn, the pitch you hear will be **different** — it'll be **lower** if the car is moving **away** from you and **higher** if it's moving **towards** you. This is the **Doppler effect**.

3) When the car is moving **away** from you, the sound waves travel in the **opposite** direction from the car, so are **stretched** out — i.e. have a **longer wavelength** and **lower frequency** when they reach you.

4) The opposite happens when the car is moving **towards** you — the sound waves **bunch up**, so have a **shorter wavelength** and **higher frequency** when they get to you.

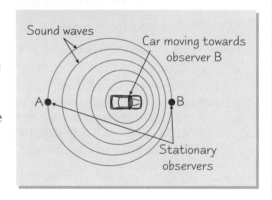

Not all police forces use radar guns to catch speeding motorists.

5) How much the sound waves change depends on how **fast** the car is travelling — the **greater** the car's **speed**, the **larger** the **change**. This means the Doppler effect can be used to **measure the speed** of moving objects.

6) The Doppler effect happens with **all waves**, so it has a wide range of applications. For example, **police radar guns** measure the speed of cars using **microwaves**, while **ultrasound sonography** is used to monitor the function of **blood vessels** by measuring how fast **blood** is flowing inside them.

Ultrasound Imaging

Shorter Wavelengths Produce Clearer Images

Ultrasound scanning can be a really useful technique — but only if the images are **clear**.
The **properties** of the ultrasound **radiation** used has a big effect on the clarity of the images produced.

1) **Shorter** wavelengths **diffract** (see page 84) much **less** than longer wavelengths.

2) This means that the shorter the **wavelength** of the ultrasound, the less the waves **spread out** as they travel and the more **precisely** the location of the interfaces between tissues can be mapped.

3) So ultrasound scanners use waves with a **high frequency** and **short wavelength**.

Shorter Pulses Produce Clearer Images

Ultrasound transducers cannot **transmit** and **receive** pulses at the same time. If **reflected** waves reach the transducer while it is **transmitting**, the information they contain will be **lost** and image **quality** will be reduced. This means:

1) The **pulses** of ultrasound transmitted must be **very short** (a few microseconds long) so that the reflections from nearby interfaces don't reach the transducer before the pulse has ended.

2) The gap between pulses must be **long** (at least 1 millisecond) so that all the reflected waves from one pulse return to the transducer **before** the next pulse is transmitted.

Developments in Science and Technology Have Social and Ethical Issues

When scientists work, they have to consider whether what they want to achieve is possible and whether it **should** be done at all. For example, when deciding whether a **medical technique** should be used, scientists consider:

1) **Safety** — will the technique cause more **harm** than **good**? For example, an **X-ray** might show up a problem that an ultrasound scan cannot, but X-rays are known to **damage cells** whereas ultrasound is not (so far).

2) **Social issues** — will the technique **benefit society** or adversely affect people? For example, ultrasound scans of **unborn foetuses** allow doctors to spot problems or abnormal growth, giving them a chance to **put it right**.

3) **Ethical issues** — is the technique **morally right**? Will it lead to dangerous new developments? For example, ultrasound scans can be used to show the **gender** of foetuses, but this might lead to **unnecessary** terminations.

4) **Cost** — do the **benefits** of the technique outweigh the **expense**? For example, **MRI scanning** is less dangerous than **X-ray imaging** and gives clearer pictures than ultrasound, but is much more **expensive** than either.

Practice Questions

Q1 What is an interface? What happens to a wave when it reaches an interface?

Q2 How is sonar similar to ultrasound scanning?

Q3 State and explain two things you can do to improve the clarity of an ultrasound image.

Exam Questions

Q1 Ultrasound scans can be used to measure the rate of blood flow within a person's body. The diagram shows the ultrasound wave transmitted into a patient.

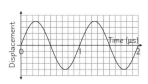

(a) Sketch the ultrasound wave reflected from blood flowing towards the receiver. [1 mark]

(b) Sketch the ultrasound wave reflected from blood flowing away from the receiver. [1 mark]

Q2 Describe and explain two social/ethical issues concerning a manned space mission to Mars. [4 marks]

I've got social issues — no one likes me...

*An interesting fact for you — Christian Doppler (of Doppler effect fame) lived practically next door to Mozart.
Except that Mozart travelled all around the world and died before Doppler was born, but they're just minor details.*

The Electromagnetic Spectrum

These pages are for AQA A Unit 2, Edexcel Unit 2 and OCR A Unit 2.

There's nothing really deep and meaningful to understand on this page — just a load of facts to learn I'm afraid.

All **Electromagnetic Waves** Have Some **Properties** In Common

1) They travel in a **vacuum** at a **speed** of **2.998×10^8 ms^{-1}**, and at slower speeds in other media.
2) They are **transverse** waves consisting of **vibrating electric** and **magnetic fields**.
   The **electric** and **magnetic** fields are at **right angles** to each other and to the **direction of travel**.
3) Like all waves, EM waves can be **reflected**, **refracted** and **diffracted** and can undergo **interference**.
4) Like all waves, EM waves obey $v = f\lambda$ (v = velocity, f = frequency, λ = wavelength).
5) Like all progressive waves, progressive EM waves **carry energy**.
6) Like all transverse waves, EM waves can be **polarised**.

Some **Properties Vary** Across the **EM Spectrum**

EM waves with different wavelengths behave differently in some respects. The spectrum is split into seven categories: **radio waves**, **microwaves**, **infrared**, **visible light**, **ultraviolet**, **X-rays** and **gamma rays**.

1) The longer the wavelength, the more **obvious** the wave characteristics — e.g., long radio waves diffract round hills.
2) **Energy** is directly proportional to **frequency**. **Gamma rays** have the **highest energy**; **radio waves** the **lowest**.
3) The **higher** the **energy**, in general the more **dangerous** the wave.
4) The **lower the energy** of an EM wave, the **further from the nucleus** it comes from. **Gamma radiation** comes from inside the **nucleus**. **X-rays to visible light** come from energy-level transitions in **atoms** (see p. 94). **Infrared** radiation and **microwaves** are associated with **molecules**. **Radio waves** come from oscillations in **electric fields**.

The **Properties** of an **EM Wave** Change with **Wavelength**

Type	Approximate wavelength / m	Penetration	Uses
Radio waves	10^{-1} — 10^6	Pass through matter.	Radio transmissions.
Microwaves	10^{-3} — 10^{-1}	Mostly pass through matter, but cause some heating.	Radar. Microwave cookery. TV transmissions.
Infrared (IR)	7×10^{-7} — 10^{-3}	Mostly absorbed by matter, causing it to heat up.	Heat detectors. Night-vision cameras. Remote controls. Optical fibres.
Visible light	4×10^{-7} — 7×10^{-7}	Absorbed by matter, causing some heating effect.	Human sight. Optical fibres.
Ultraviolet (UV)	10^{-8} — 4×10^{-7}	Absorbed by matter. Slight ionisation.	Sunbeds. Security markings that show up in UV light.
X-rays	10^{-13} — 10^{-8}	Mostly pass through matter, but cause ionisation as they pass.	To see damage to bones and teeth. Airport security scanners. To kill cancer cells.
Gamma rays	10^{-16} — 10^{-10}	Mostly pass through matter, but cause ionisation as they pass.	Irradiation of food. Sterilisation of medical instruments. To kill cancer cells.

The Electromagnetic Spectrum

Different Types of EM Wave Have Different Effects on the Body

Type	Production	Effect on human body
Radio waves	Oscillating electrons in an aerial	No effect.
Microwaves	Electron tube oscillators. Masers.	Absorbed by water — danger of cooking human body*.
Infrared (IR)	Natural and artificial heat sources.	Heating. Excess heat can harm the body's systems.
Visible light	Natural and artificial light sources.	Used for sight. Too bright a light can damage eyes.
Ultraviolet (UV)	e.g. the Sun.	Tans the skin. Can cause skin cancer and eye damage.
X-rays	Bombarding metal with electrons.	Cancer due to cell damage. Eye damage.
Gamma rays	Radioactive decay of the nucleus.	Cancer due to cell damage. Eye damage.

OCR A Unit 2 only

* Or small animals.

1) UV radiation is split into categories based on frequency — **UV-A**, **UV-B** and **UV-C**.

2) **UV-A** has the **lowest** frequency and is the **least damaging**, although it's thought to be a significant cause of **skin aging**.

3) Higher-frequency **UV-B** is more dangerous. It can be **absorbed** by DNA molecules, causing **mutations** which can lead to **cancer**. UV-B is responsible for **sunburn** too.

4) **UV-C** has a high enough frequency to be **ionising** — it carries enough energy to knock electrons off atoms. This can cause **cell mutation** or **destruction**, and **cancer**. It's almost **entirely blocked** by the ozone layer, though.

5) **Dark** skin gives some protection from UV rays, stopping them reaching more vulnerable tissues below. So **tanning** is a protection mechanism — **UV-A** triggers the release of melanin (a brown pigment) in the skin.

6) **Sunscreens** provide some protection from UV in sunlight. The **Sun Protection Factor (SPF)** of the sunscreen tells you how well it protects against **UV-B** radiation. It **doesn't** tell you anything about the UV-A protection though. Many modern sunscreens include tiny particles of **zinc oxide** and **titanium dioxide** to block UV-A.

Practice Questions

Q1 What are the main practical uses of infrared radiation?
Q2 Which types of electromagnetic radiation have the highest and lowest energies?
Q3 What is the significance of the speed 2.998×10^8 ms^{-1}?
Q4 Why are microwaves dangerous?
Q5 How does the energy of an EM wave vary with frequency?

Exam Questions

Q1 In a vacuum, do X-rays travel faster, slower or at the same speed as visible light? Explain your answer. [2 marks]

Q2 (a) Describe briefly the physics behind a practical use of X rays. [2 marks]
(b) What is the difference between gamma rays and X-rays? [2 marks]

Q3 Give an example of a type of electromagnetic wave causing a hazard to health. [2 marks]

I've got UV hair...

No really I have. It's great. It's purple. And it's got shiny glittery white bits in it.
Aaaanyway... moving swiftly on. Loads of facts to learn on these pages. You probably know most of this from GCSE anyway, but make sure you know it well enough to answer a question on it in the exam. Not much fun, but... there you go.

Information in Images

These pages are for OCR B Unit 1 only.
Don't panic if waves are getting a bit too much for you — it's time for something completely different.

Decimal	Binary
0	0
1	1
2	10
3	11

A *Single Binary Digit* is Called a *Bit*

1) The **binary number system**, like the **decimal** system, is a way of writing numbers.
2) The difference is that the **decimal** system uses **ten digits** (0-9) while the **binary** system only uses **two** (**0 and 1**). The table shows the first few values in each system.
3) The **zeros** and **ones** that make up binary numbers are called **binary digits** — a **single binary digit** is called a **bit**. A group of **eight binary digits** is called a **byte**.

The *Binary System* is used to Store *Data* in *Computer Memory*

1) When you **save** a file on your computer, the computer stores the data as a **string of bits**.
2) The **number of bits** in a string (I) determines how many **alternatives** that string can code for. For example, a **single** bit has only **two** alternatives (0 and 1), while one **byte** (eight bits) has **256** alternatives. The number of alternatives **doubles** with each additional bit, which means:

$$\text{Number of alternatives} = 2^{\text{Number of bits}} \text{ or } N = 2^I$$

Bytes are the smallest meaningful units of computer memory.

3) The **number of bits** you need depends on how many **alternatives** you want:

$$\text{Number of bits} = \log_2(\text{number of alternatives}) \text{ or } I = \log_2 N$$

For example, if you wanted to code for any letter of the **alphabet**, you'd need a string with **26 alternatives** — one for every letter. Substituting 26 into the **equation** gives $I = \log_2 26 \approx 4.7$ — so you'd need **five bits**.

Images Are Stored as *Arrays* of *Binary Numbers*

1) If you **zoom** in on part of a **digital photograph**, you'll see the individual **pixels** (squares of colour) that make up the image — check out the example on the right. ➡
2) When an **image** is stored in a digital camera (e.g. on a **memory card**) or on a **computer**, each pixel is represented by a **binary number**.
3) The **binary numbers** are stored in an **array**. They're arranged so that the **location** of a **number** in the grid **matches** the location in the photo of the **pixel** it describes.
4) The **value** of the binary number gives the **colour** (or shade of grey) of the corresponding **pixel**. For example, the **image** shown is made up of **256 shades** of grey — each one is represented by an **eight-digit** binary number.
5) In **coloured images**, each pixel can be described by **three** binary numbers — one for each of the **primary colours** of light (**red**, **green** and **blue**). The **length** of the binary numbers used depends on **how many** colours are needed.

Multiplying by a Fixed Value *Improves Contrast*

The **values** of the binary numbers that make up an **image** determine how it looks — if you **change** the **values**, you **change** the **image**. Take a look at the **example** below to see what happens.

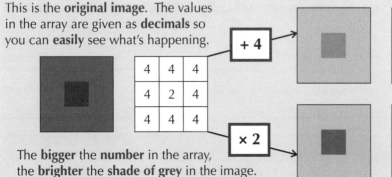

This is the **original image**. The values in the array are given as **decimals** so you can **easily** see what's happening.

4	4	4
4	2	4
4	4	4

+ 4

8	8	8
8	6	8
8	8	8

Adding a fixed positive value makes the image **brighter**, but it **doesn't change** the **difference** between the **dark** and **light** regions (**contrast**).

× 2

8	8	8
8	4	8
8	8	8

Mulitplying by a fixed value (greater than 1) makes the image **brighter**, and **increases** the **contrast**.

The **bigger** the **number** in the array, the **brighter** the **shade of grey** in the image.

Information in Images

Adding *False Colour* Highlights Features

In the example on the last page, a value of '**2**' in the array mapped to a **dark shade of grey** in the image, while a value of '**4**' mapped to a slightly **brighter shade**. But you could map '**2**' to a **dark shade of pink** and '**4**' to a **brighter shade** — or '**2**' to **orange** and '**4**' to **green**.

This process is called adding **false colour**. You can use **any** colours you like, but they're usually picked to **highlight certain features** — e.g. the **important features** could be made a really **bright** colour.

You can transform an image by changing the colours that the values in its array map to — not the array itself.

Replacing Pixels *With the* Median *of their Neighbours* Reduces Noise

This array would show a bright spot, in a uniform, darker region — the spot is probably noise.

2	3	2
1	12	2
2	2	1

→

2	3	2
1	2	2
2	2	1

Replacing the central value with the median of all nine values evens out the brightness of the region.

1) **Noise** is **unwanted interference** affecting a signal. In images this is usually **bright** or **dark** spots on the picture.

2) One way you can get rid of **noise** is to **replace** each pixel with the **median** of itself and the eight pixels surrounding it.

3) The result is that any '**odd**' (i.e. very **high** or very **low**) values are **removed** and the image is **smoother**.

The *Laplace Rule* is Used to *Find Edges*

If you're trying to work out if there is **something** in your image (rather than just a load of **noise**), finding any **edges** can be a really **useful** first step.

The **Laplace rule** is a method of **finding edges**. To apply the rule, you **multiply** a pixel by **four**, then **subtract** the value of the pixels immediately **above**, **below**, to the **left** and to the **right** of it.

The result is that any pixel **not** on an **edge** goes **black** — so you're left with **just** the edges.

The Laplace rule will only highlight an edge if there is a steep change in brightness (i.e. an edge). If the change is gradual (i.e. not an edge), the rule will smooth the change in brightness, making it less noticeable.

Practice Questions

Q1 What's the difference between a bit and a byte?

Q2 How can the brightness of an image be changed?

Q3 How can the contrast of an image by improved?

Q4 What is the Laplace rule used for? How do you apply it?

Exam Questions

Q1 The diagram shows part of an array that describes an image. The image is made up of 256 shades of grey — 0 represents black and 255 represents white.

100	99	100
97	185	98
101	101	98

(a) Sketch the image that this part of the array describes. [1 mark]

(b) Describe how noise can be removed from digital images. [1 mark]

(b) Apply this technique to the central value of the array shown. [1 mark]

Q2 A television can display 65 536 different colours.

(a) What is the minimum number of bits needed to store the colour of each pixel? [1 mark]

(b) How many bytes is this? [1 mark]

All this talk of bytes is making me hungry — mmm, tasty bites...

These two pages (and the next few) are a bit of a detour from the 'proper' Physics they taught in my day — where are all the complicated mathematical equations and boring diagrams to get lost in? It's just not right. If I had my way, I'd... well...

Sampling

These pages are for OCR B Unit 1 only.

You've just seen how information can be stored digitally, but what if you want to send that information? And what if the information isn't digital to start with? So many questions — read on to find out the answers.

Analogue Signals Vary Continuously

1) **Digital signals**, like the images on the previous page, are represented by **binary numbers**.

2) The **values** that a **digital signal** can take depend on the **number of bits** used — e.g. a **one bit** signal can only take the values **0 and 1**, but a **one byte** signal can take **256 different values**.

3) **Analogue signals** are **not limited** in the values they can take — they **vary continuously**. For example, **speech** is an **analogue signal** — the **sound waves** produced **vary continuously** over a range of **loudness** and **frequency**.

Digital Signals Are Resistant to the Effects of Noise

When you **transmit** an electronic signal it will pick up **noise** (interference) from **electrical disturbances** or other **signals**. The receiver needs to be able to **reconstruct** the **original signal** from the **noisy signal** if they're to get an **accurate representation** of what was sent. This is **much easier** with **digital** than analogue signals because the **number of values** a digital signal can take is **limited**.

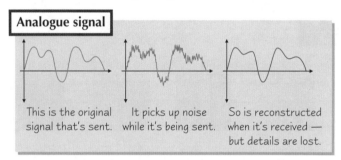

Analogue signal

This is the original signal that's sent.   It picks up noise while it's being sent.   So is reconstructed when it's received — but details are lost.

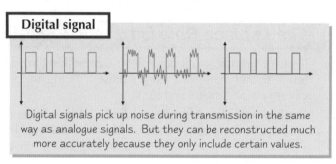

Digital signal

Digital signals pick up noise during transmission in the same way as analogue signals. But they can be reconstructed much more accurately because they only include certain values.

Analogue Signals can be Digitised

1) It's possible to turn an **analogue signal** into a **digital signal** — this is called **digitising** the signal.

2) To digitise a signal, you take the **value** of the signal at **regular time intervals**, then find the **nearest digital value**.

3) Each **digital value** is represented by a **binary number**, so you can **convert** the **analogue** values to **binary** numbers.

4) The **digital signal** you end up with won't be **exactly** the same as the **analogue signal**, but it's usually quite **close**.

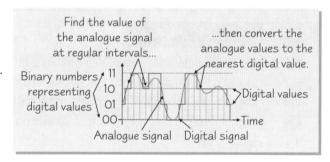

Find the value of the analogue signal at regular intervals... ...then convert the analogue values to the nearest digital value.

Binary numbers representing digital values { 11, 10, 01, 00 }   Digital values   Time

Analogue signal   Digital signal

The Quality of a Digitised Signal Depends on Its Resolution

1) How well a **digitised** signal matches the original depends on **two** factors — the **difference** between the possible **digital values** (**resolution**) and the **time** from one **sample** to the next (**sampling rate**, see p73).

2) If a signal is digitised using only a **few, widely spaced** digital values, it's likely that a lot of the analogue values sampled will be **far** from the **nearest digital value**. But, if a **large** number of **closely spaced** digital values are used, most of the analogue values will be **very close** to a digital value, so will only change **slightly**.

3) This means that the **higher the resolution** (i.e. the **more possible digital values** there are), the **more closely** the digitised signal will **match** the original.

4) **Resolution** is determined by the **number of bits** in the **binary numbers** representing the digital values — the **greater** the number of **bits**, the **greater** the **resolution**.

5) When **music** is digitised to make **CDs** a resolution of **16 bits** is used. This gives a total of **65 536 digital values** and means the recorded music is **very similar** to the **original**.

Sampling

Noise Limits the Number of Bits used for Sampling

You've just seen that the **higher the resolution**, the **better** a digitised signal **matches** the original. But, if the original signal contains **noise** (as most real signals do), then a really **fine resolution** will reproduce all the little wiggles caused by the **noise** — **not useful**. In practice, the **resolution** is **limited** by the **ratio** of the total **variation** in the **signal** to the **variation** caused by **noise**:

$$Maximum\ number\ of\ bits = \log_2\left(\frac{Total\ variation}{Noise\ variation}\right) \quad or \quad b = \log_2\left(\frac{V_{total}}{V_{noise}}\right)$$

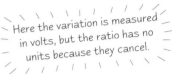
Here the variation is measured in volts, but the ratio has no units because they cancel.

Minimum Sampling Rate is Twice the Maximum Frequency

1) When you **digitise** a signal, you **record the value** of (**sample**) the original signal at **regular intervals**. The **rate** at which you **sample** the signal is called the **sampling rate** — imaginative name, I know.

2) The **sampling rate** has to be **high** enough to record all the **high frequency** detail of the signal. The diagram on the **right** shows how **detail** can be **lost** if the sampling rate is too **low**.

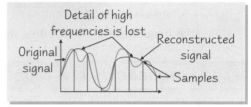
Detail of high frequencies is lost — Reconstructed signal — Original signal — Samples

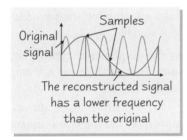
Samples — Original signal — The reconstructed signal has a lower frequency than the original

3) Worse still, a **low** sampling rate can **create** low frequency signals — called **aliases** — that **weren't** in the original signal at all. The diagram on the **left** shows how **aliases** can be **created** by a **low sampling rate**.

4) To avoid these problems, the **sampling rate** must be at least **twice** the **highest frequency** in the original signal.

Minimum rate of sampling = 2 × maximum frequency of signal

Digital Signals Have Four Main Advantages Over Analogue Signals

1) Digital signals can be **sent**, **received** and **reproduced** more easily than analogue signals because they can only take a limited number of values.

2) Digital signals are **resistant** to the effects of **noise** — analogue signals are **negatively affected** by **noise**.

3) Digital signals can be used to represent **different** kinds of **information** in the **same way** — for example, **images** and **sounds** can both be represented as a string of bits.

4) Digital signals are **easy to process** using **computers**, since computers are **digital devices** too.

But, digital signals can **never** reproduce analogue signals **exactly** — some **information** will always be **lost**.

Practice Questions

Q1 Explain how a digital signal is different from an analogue one.

Q2 What is meant by resolution in the context of digitising analogue signals?

Q3 Describe two problems that can be caused by an insufficient sampling rate.

Q4 Give four advantages of digital signals over analogue.

Exam Questions

Q1 A digital signal has a total variation of 160 mV and a noise variation of 10 mV.
What is the maximum number of bits that should be used when sampling this signal? [2 marks]

Q2 An analogue signal contains frequencies at 100 Hz, 500 Hz, 310 Hz and 250 Hz.
What is the minimum sampling rate that should be used when digitising this signal? [1 mark]

How do finger puppets communicate? With digital signals...

Digital signals are everywhere these days — CDs, MP3s, DVDs, digital TV — there's just no escape. Analogue signals are still around, though — some people prefer them for listening to music and use vinyl (ask your dad) instead of CDs.

Signal Spectra and Bandwidth

These pages are for OCR B Unit 1 only.

I'm very sorry about the 'joke' on the previous page — the person responsible has been summoned to a meeting of the International Humour Committee to explain themselves. For the rest of us, it's back to the wonderful world of signals...

Signals are Made Up of Lots of Different Frequencies

1) If you were asked to draw a **wave**, you'd probably sketch a **sine curve** (like the one on page 62). This is the **simplest** kind of **signal** because it contains just **one frequency**.

2) In practice, most **signals** are made up of **several** sine curves, all with **different frequencies**, added together. For example, if you play a **musical note**, the sound you hear contains the **frequency** (pitch) of the **main note** and a load of **other frequencies**. It's these 'other frequencies' that make instruments **sound different**, even though they're playing the **same note**.

3) The **frequencies** that **make up** a **signal** are called its **spectrum**.

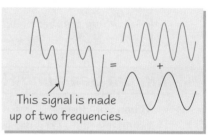

This signal is made up of two frequencies.

The Frequencies in a Signal Contain Information

If you want to **reconstruct** a signal, you need to know about **all** of the **frequencies** within it. All the frequencies in a signal carry **information**, so if you **lose** any of the frequencies, you **won't** get all the **information** from the signal. This is why the **sampling rate** (see page 73) is so important when **digitising** analogue signals.

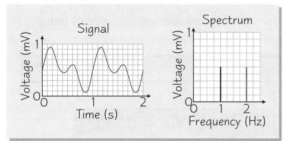

You can get information about the **frequencies** within a **signal** by **drawing** a graph of its **spectrum**. The graph shows the **amplitude** and **frequency** of **all** the waves that make up the signal.

The signal shown on the **left** is the same as the one **above**. The **two peaks** on the **spectrum** correspond to the **two frequencies** that make up the signal.

Most **signals** are made up of **several** frequencies with different amplitudes — their **spectra** would have **more**, **different sized peaks**.

Bandwidth is the Range of Frequencies within a Signal

You've just seen that a signal's **spectrum** is all the **frequencies** within the signal. The **range** that a **signal's spectrum** covers is called its **bandwidth**. You can find a signal's **bandwidth** by **subtracting** the **lowest frequency** within it from the **highest frequency** — or by looking at the **graph** of its **spectrum**.

The **bandwidth** of the **signal** in the examples above is: 2 Hz – 1 Hz = **1 Hz**.

In **communications** systems the **bandwidth** of each signal determines **how many** signals can be sent at the **same time** (see page 75 for an explanation).

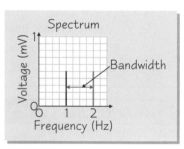

Communication Signals Are Transmitted Using Carrier Waves

1) When you **tune** a **radio** you scan through the **frequencies** it's receiving until you find the one you want. What you are searching for is the **frequency** of the **carrier wave** that **transmits** the signal from your station.

2) At the radio station, the **audio signal** from the presenter or music is converted to an **electronic signal**. This **signal** is then mixed with a **carrier wave**, and the combined signal is **transmitted**.

3) When your **radio** is tuned to the **right frequency**, it **receives** the **signal** from the radio station. It is able to **separate** the **actual signal** from the **carrier wave** and then convert this back into **sound** for you to listen to.

4) All **radio stations** are given a particular **carrier frequency** to broadcast their signal on. The **carrier frequencies** of all the stations in a local area have to be **different** so that they don't **interfere** with each other.

5) It's **not** just radio that uses this system — for example, **television** and **mobile telephone signals** are sent in the **same** way. The difference is that the **carrier frequencies** used for each system lie in **different parts** of the **electromagnetic spectrum** (see page 68).

Signal Spectra and Bandwidth

Bandwidth Limits the Number of Signals that can be Transmitted

1) You've just seen that **radio stations** have to use **different** carrier frequencies so they don't **interfere** with each other. But there also has to be a **gap** between the **frequencies** used — for example, if 'Little FM' broadcasts with a frequency of 107.3 MHz, you **won't** find another station at 107.2 MHz or 107.4 MHz.

2) The **size** of the **gap** between frequencies is determined by the **bandwidth** of the **audio signal** — the **larger** the **bandwidth**, the **larger** the **gap** must be to **stop** signals at neighbouring carrier frequencies **overlapping**.

3) In practice, the **carrier frequencies** for radio stations are always **at least** 0.2 MHz apart and the signals are **filtered** (very high or low frequencies are removed) to make sure they **don't** exceed this range.

4) The **problem** with having gaps between the carrier frequencies is that it **limits** the **number of signals** that can be transmitted. For example, **FM radio** can be transmitted between **30 MHz and 300 MHz**. So with a gap of 0.2 MHz, there's **only** space for (300 − 30) ÷ 0.2 = **1350 stations**.

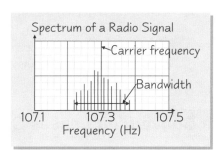

Spectrum of a Radio Signal
Carrier frequency
Bandwidth
107.1   107.3   107.5
Frequency (Hz)

Rate of Transmission = Samples per Second × Bits per Sample

By now you should know **how** signals are **transmitted** — what's also important is the **rate** at which they're transmitted. The **rate of transmission** of a digital signal depends on **two** factors:

1) The number of **samples per second** — this must be at least **twice** the **highest frequency** in the signal to ensure that all the frequencies within its spectrum are transmitted accurately.

2) The number of **bits per sample** — this must be **high enough** that the transmitted signal **closely** matches the original, but not so high that it is negatively affected by **noise**.

Rate of transmission of a digital signal (bits per second) = *samples per second* × *bits per sample*

Practice Questions

Q1   What is meant by a) the spectrum and b) the bandwidth of a signal?

Q2   What are carrier signals used for?

Q3   Why is the number of signals that can be transmitted at the same time limited?

Exam Questions

Q1   The telephone system samples your voice 8000 times a second and converts this into an eight bit digital signal.

(a) What is the rate of transmission for bits in this telephone system?   [1 mark]

(b) How many bytes are sent each second?   [1 mark]

Q2   The diagram shows the spectrum of a signal.

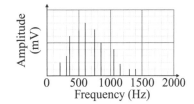

Amplitude (mV)

0   500 1000 1500 2000
Frequency (Hz)

(a) What does the spectrum of a signal show?   [1 mark]

(b) What is the bandwidth of this signal?   [1 mark]

Bandwidth — the diameter of the drum kit...

Congratulations — you've made it through the pages on signalling. I don't know about you, but I think I'm going to celebrate with a nice cup of tea and a biscuit. Oh, wait, I should probably write up the answers to those pesky exam questions first.

Forming Images with Lenses

These pages are for OCR B Unit 1 only.

Astronomers use focal lengths, opticians use powers. Either way, you need to know how to deal with lens powers...

Refraction Happens when a Wave Changes Speed at a Boundary

1) When a ray of light meets a boundary between one medium and another, some of its energy is **reflected** back into the first medium and the rest of it is **transmitted** through into the second medium.

2) If the light meets the boundary at an angle to the normal, the transmitted ray is bent or "**refracted**" as it travels at a **different speed** in each medium.
The more **optically dense** a material is, the more slowly light travels in it.

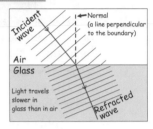

Converging Lenses Change the Curvature of Wavefronts

1) **Lenses** change the curvature of wavefronts by **refraction**.

2) A lens **adds curvature** to waves as they pass through it. If waves are uncurved before passing through the lens, and parallel to the lens axis, they will be given spherical curvature, centred on the **focus** (or **focal point**) of the lens.

3) The lens curves the wavefronts by **slowing down** the light travelling through the middle of the lens for longer than light at the lens edges. All points on a wavefront takes the **same amount of time** to get to the focus point (see p 101).

4) The **focal length**, f, is the distance between the **lens axis** and the **focus**.

5) The **more powerful** (thicker) the lens, the more **strongly** it will **curve** the wavefronts that travel through it — so the **shorter** its focal length.

6) The **power** of a lens with focal length f m is: where lens power is measured in **dioptres**, **D**.

$$P = \frac{1}{f}$$

7) The curvature of a wave is defined as:

$$\text{curvature} = \frac{1}{\text{radius of curvature}}$$

So the **amount of curvature** a lens adds to a wave passing through it is $1/f$... which is just the **power** of the lens.

You can also show image formation with **ray diagrams**.

You can use the Lens Equation to Find Where an Image Will be Formed

1) The distances between the lens, the image and the source are related to each other by **the lens equation**:

$$\frac{1}{v} = \frac{1}{u} + \frac{1}{f}$$

u = distance between object and lens axis,
v = distance between image and lens axis,
f = focal length.

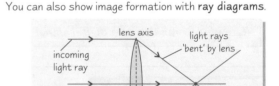

2) You always measure the **distances** from the **lens axis**, and count distances to the **right** as **positive**, and distances to the **left** as **negative** — just like when you're drawing graphs.

3) The lens equation also tells you about **curvature**.

4) So, if you've got a **distant source**, the wavefronts will be **flat** ($1/u = 0$) and the lens will give them a curvature of $1/f$. Easy.

curvature after =	curvature before +	curvature added by lens
$(1/v)$	$(1/u)$	$(1/f)$

5) If the source is at the **focal point** of the lens, you'll probably have a **negatively curved** (as the radius is a negative distance) wavefront before the light reaches the lens, which will be made **flat** once its passed through the lens.

6) For sources in between, the wavefronts before and after will be curved, and have a difference in curvature of $1/f$.

7) Don't forget that you can also draw all this in the form of **light rays** being 'bent' by the lens. It's just a different way of thinking about it — you still use the lens equation in exactly the same way.

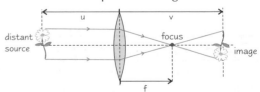

Forming Images with Lenses

Example

An image of Mabel the cow is being projected onto a screen 80 cm from a 3.25 D lens. How far must the picture slide of Mabel be from the lens?

$P = \dfrac{1}{f} = 3.25$ D, $v = 80$ cm $= 0.8$ m

Rearrange the lens equation: $\dfrac{1}{u} = \dfrac{1}{v} - \dfrac{1}{f} = \dfrac{1}{0.8} - 3.25 = 1.25 - 3.25 = -2$

$u = -\dfrac{1}{2} = -0.5$ m, so the slide must be $\underline{0.5\ m}$ from the lens.

A Lens Can Produce a **Magnified Image**

There are a couple of ways of measuring the magnification of a lens.
You just need to know about the **linear magnification**.

The **linear magnification** of a lens is $\boxed{m = \dfrac{\text{size of image}}{\text{size of object}}}$, which is equal to $\boxed{m = \dfrac{v}{u}}$.

Practice Questions

Q1 Define the focal length and power of a converging lens.

Q2 Write an equation to show how the object distance (*u*), image distance (*v*) and focal length (*f*) are related.

Q3 Describe what happens to wavefronts as they pass through a thin converging lens.

Q4 A wave passed through a thin converging lens with a focal length f.
If the wavefronts had no curvature before entering the lens, what is their curvature after passing through the lens?

Exam Questions

Q1 (a) Define the *focal point* and the *focal length* of a converging lens. [2 marks]

(b) An object was placed 0.20 m in front of a converging lens of focal length 0.15 m.
How far behind the lens was the image formed? [2 marks]

Q2 The length of a seed is 12.5 mm. A lens is placed in front of the seed, so that the axis of the lens is parallel to the seed. An image of the seed is projected onto a screen. The image has a length of 47.2 mm.

(a) Find the linear magnification of the lens. [1 mark]

(b) If the seed is 4 mm from the lens, how far is the screen from the lens? [2 marks]

(c) Calculate the power of the lens in dioptres. [3 marks]

By the power of Grayskull... I HAVE THE POWER...

This is all fairly straightforward — just a few formulas. But it's a great one for experiment-based questions in the exam, so make sure you know how to deal with uncertainties and error bars. See page 114 for stuff on error analysis.

Refractive Index

These pages are for AQA A Unit 2, Edexcel Unit 2 and OCR B Unit 1 (just the first definition).

Pages 62-65 cover the basics of what waves are. This stuff explains why your legs look short in a swimming pool.

The **Refractive Index** of a Material Measures **How Much** It Slows Down Light

Light goes fastest in a **vacuum**. It **slows down** in other materials, because it **interacts** with the particles in them. The more **optically dense** a material is, the more light slows down when it enters it.

The **absolute refractive index** of a material, **n**, is the **ratio** between the **speed of light** in a **vacuum**, **c**, and the speed of light in that **material**, **v**. (If you're doing **OCR B**, this definition's all you need to know.)

$$n = \frac{c}{v}$$ $c = 3 \times 10^8 \, ms^{-1}$

Edexcel give the refractive index the symbol μ instead of n.

The **relative** refractive index **between two materials**, $_1n_2$, is the ratio of the speed of light **in material 1** to the speed of light **in material 2**.

$$_1n_2 = \frac{v_1}{v_2}$$

Combining the two equations gives: $$_1n_2 = \frac{n_2}{n_1}$$

The speed of light in air is only a tiny bit smaller than c. So you can assume the refractive index of air is 1.

1) The **absolute refractive index** of a material is a **property** of that material only. But a **relative refractive index** is a property of the **interface** between two materials. It's different for **every possible pair**.

2) Because you can assume $n_{air} = 1$, you can assume the refractive index for an **air to glass boundary** equals the **absolute refractive index** of the glass.

Snell's Law uses Angles to Calculate the Refractive Index

1) The **angle** the **incoming light** makes to the **normal** is called the **angle of incidence, i**. The **angle** the **refracted ray** makes with the **normal** is the **angle of refraction, r**.

2) When light enters an optically denser medium it is refracted **towards** the normal.

3) **n**, **i** and **r** are related by **Snell's law**.

$$n_1 \sin i = n_2 \sin r$$

You don't need to know the geometry of why Snell's law works, but you need to be able to use it.

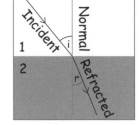

4) You can use a device called a **refractometer** to accurately measure the refractive index of a material. The machine shines a beam of light at the sample. You then view the refracted beam through a **microscope** and measure its angle of refraction.

Sometimes You Need to Know Refractive Index **Very Accurately**

1) **Making lenses** — There are several different types of glass that can be used to make lenses, and they all have different refractive indices. The refractive index of the glass affects how thick and how curved the lens has to be to get the same magnifying power.
It's important to know the refractive index accurately so you can calculate the exact shape of lens to fit, say, someone's prescription for a pair of glasses.

2) **In forensic investigations** — identifying broken bits of glass and plastic can be vital when tracking down crime suspects. Once you know the exact refractive index of the glass from the crime scene, you can compare it with shards found on the clothes or shoes of a suspect. Most shards are too small for a refractometer, so you need to measure the refractive index differently. You use the fact that if two materials with the same refractive index are side by side, you can't see the boundary between them.

Refractive Index

Light Leaving an **Optically Denser Material** is Refracted **Away** from the **Normal**

When light **goes from** an optically denser material into an optically **less dense** material (e.g. glass to air), interesting things can start to happen.

Shine a ray of light at a **glass to air** boundary, then gradually **increase** the angle of incidence. As you increase the angle of incidence, the angle of **refraction** gets closer and closer to **90°**. Eventually *i* reaches a **critical angle C** for which *r* = **90°**. The light is **refracted** along the **boundary**.

At this **critical angle**, Snell's law $n_{glass} \sin i = n_{air} \sin r$ becomes:

$n \sin C = 1$ so: $$n = \frac{1}{\sin C}$$

That's because the refractive index of air is 1 and sin 90° = 1

At angles of incidence **greater than C** refraction is **impossible**. That means **all** the light is reflected back into the material. This effect is called **total internal reflection**.

Optical Fibres Use Total Internal Reflection

1) An optical fibre is a very **thin flexible tube** of **glass** or **plastic** fibre that can carry **light signals** over long distances and round corners.

2) The optical fibres themselves have a **high refractive index** but are surrounded by **cladding** with a lower refractive index.

3) Light is shone in at **one end** of the fibre. The fibre is so **narrow** that the light always **hits the boundary** between fibre and cladding at an **angle bigger** than the **critical angle**.

4) So all the light is **totally internally reflected** from boundary to boundary until it reaches the other end.

Light running through optical fibres is used to transmit **phone and cable TV signals**. It beats the **old system** of using **electricity** flowing through **copper cables**:

1) The signal can carry **more information** because light has a high frequency.
2) The light **doesn't heat up the fibre** — so almost no energy is lost as heat.
3) There is no electrical **interference**.

Practice Questions

Q1 Why does light go fastest in a vacuum and slow down in other media?
Q2 What is the formula for the critical angle for a ray of light at a water/air boundary?

Exam Questions

Q1 (a) Light travels in diamond at 1.24×10^8 ms^{-1}. What is the refractive index of diamond? [1 mark]

(b) What is the angle of refraction if light strikes a facet of a diamond ring at an angle of 50° to the normal of the air/diamond boundary? [2 marks]

Q2 An adjustable underwater spotlight is placed on the floor of an aquarium tank. When the light points upwards at a steep angle a beam comes through the surface of the water into the air, and the tank is dimly lit. When the spotlight is placed at a shallower angle, no light comes up through the water surface, and the tank is brightly lit.

(a) Explain what is happening. [2 marks]

(b) It is found that the beam into the air disappears when the spotlight is pointed at any angle of less than 41.25° to the floor. Calculate the refractive index of water. [2 marks]

I don't care about expensive things — all I care about is wave speed...

AS Physics examiners are always saying how candidates do worst in the waves bit of the exam. You'd think they'd have something more important to worry about — third world poverty, war, Posh & Becks... But no.

Superposition and Coherence

These pages are for AQA A Unit 2, Edexcel Unit 2, OCR A Unit 2 and OCR B Unit 2.
When two waves get together, it can be either really impressive or really disappointing.

Superposition Happens When Two or More Waves Pass Through Each Other

1) At the **instant** the waves **cross**, the **displacements** due to each wave **combine**. Then **each wave** goes on its merry way. You can **see** this if **two pulses** are sent **simultaneously** from each end of a rope.

2) The **principle of superposition** says that when two or more **waves** cross, the **resultant** displacement equals the **vector sum** of the **individual** displacements.

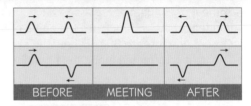

BEFORE   MEETING   AFTER

Interference can be Constructive or Destructive

1) A **crest** plus a **crest** gives a **big crest**. A **trough** plus a **trough** gives a **big trough**. These are both examples of **constructive interference**.

2) A **crest** plus a **trough** of **equal size** gives... **nothing**. The two displacements **cancel each other out** completely. This is called **destructive interference**.

3) If the **crest** and the **trough** aren't the **same size**, then the destructive interference **isn't total**. For the interference to be **noticeable**, the two **amplitudes** should be **nearly equal**.

Graphically, you can superimpose waves by adding the individual displacements at each point along the x-axis, and then plotting them.

"Superposition" means "one thing on top of another thing". You can use the same idea in reverse — a complex wave can be separated out mathematically into several simple sine waves of various sizes.

In Phase Means In Step — Two Points In Phase Interfere Constructively

1) Two points on a wave are **in phase** if they are both at the **same point** in the **wave cycle**. Points in phase have the **same displacement** and **velocity**. On the graph, points **A** and **B** are **in phase**; points **A** and **C** are **out of phase**.

2) It's mathematically **handy** to show one **complete cycle** of a wave as an **angle of 360° (2π radians)**. **Two points** with a **phase difference** of **zero** or a **multiple of 360°** are **in phase**. **Points** with a **phase difference** of odd-number multiples of **180° (π radians)** are **exactly out of phase**.

3) You can also talk about two **different waves** being **in phase**. **In practice** this happens because **both** waves came from the **same oscillator**. In **other** situations there will nearly always be a **phase difference** between two waves.

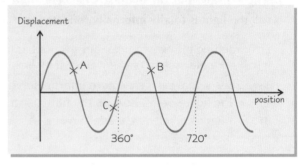

Displacement

position

360°   720°

You Can Use Phasors to Show Phase and Superposition   *OCR B only*

You can use little rotating arrows to represent the phase of each point on a wave. These arrows are called **phasors**. The phasor **rotates anticlockwise** through one whole turn as the wave completes a full cycle.

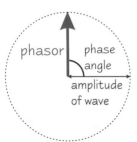

The length of the arrow shows the amplitude of the wave.

phasor   phase angle

amplitude of wave

To superimpose waves using phasors, just add the arrows tip to tail:

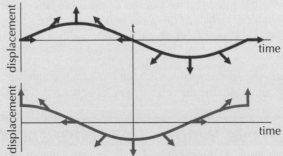

displacement   t   time

displacement   time

To find the resultant at time t, add the phasors tip to tail:

$\leftarrow + \downarrow = $ ⬊

(So in this case, the resultant wave has a greater amplitude than the component waves and is 45° out of phase with both.)

Superposition and Coherence

To Get *Interference Patterns* the *Two Sources* Must Be *Coherent*

Interference **still happens** when you're observing waves of **different wavelength** and **frequency** — but it happens in a **jumble**. In order to get clear **interference patterns**, the two or more sources must be **coherent**.

> Two sources are **coherent** if they have the **same wavelength** and **frequency** and a **fixed phase difference** between them.

In exam questions at AS, the 'fixed phase difference' is almost certainly going to be zero. The two sources will be in phase.

Constructive or *Destructive* Interference Depends on the *Path Difference*

1) Whether you get **constructive** or **destructive** interference at a **point** depends on how **much further one wave** has travelled than the **other wave** to get to that point.

2) The **amount** by which the path travelled by one wave is **longer** than the path travelled by the other wave is called the **path difference.**

3) At **any point an equal distance** from both sources you will get **constructive interference**. You also get constructive interference at any point where the **path difference** is a **whole number of wavelengths**. At these points the two waves are **in phase** and **reinforce** each other. But at points where the path difference is **half a wavelength**, **one and a half** wavelengths, **two and a half** wavelengths etc., the waves arrive **out of phase** and you get **destructive interference**.

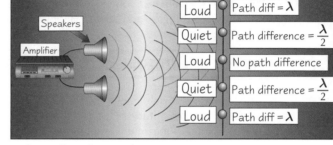

Constructive interference occurs when: | path difference = $n\lambda$ (where n is an integer)

Destructive interference occurs when: | path difference $= \dfrac{(2n+1)\lambda}{2} = (n+\frac{1}{2})\lambda$

Practice Questions

Q1 Why does the principle of superposition deal with the **vector** sum of two displacements?

Q2 What happens when a crest meets a slightly smaller trough?

Q3 If two points on a wave have a phase difference of 1440°, are they in phase?

Exam Questions

Q1 (a) Two sources are coherent.
What can you say about their frequencies, wavelengths and phase difference? [2 marks]

(b) Suggest why you might have difficulty in observing interference patterns in an area affected by two waves from two sources even though the two sources are coherent. [1 mark]

Q2 Two points on an undamped wave are exactly out of phase.

(a) What is the phase difference between them, expressed in degrees? [1 mark]

(b) Compare the displacements and velocities of the two points. [2 marks]

Learn this and you'll be in a super position to pass your exam... ...I'll get my coat.

There are a few really crucial concepts here: a) interference can be constructive or destructive, b) constructive interference happens when the path difference is a whole number of wavelengths, c) the sources must be coherent.

Stationary (Standing) Waves

These pages are for AQA A Unit 2, Edexcel Unit 2, OCR A Unit 2 and OCR B Unit 2.

Standing waves are waves that... er... stand still... well, not still exactly... I mean, well... they don't go anywhere... um...

You get Standing Waves When a **Progressive Wave** is **Reflected** at a **Boundary**

A standing wave is the **superposition** of **two progressive waves** with the **same wavelength**, moving in **opposite directions**.

1) Unlike progressive waves, **no energy** is transmitted by a standing wave.

2) You can demonstrate standing waves by setting up a **driving oscillator** at one end of a **stretched string** with the other end fixed. The wave generated by the oscillator is **reflected** back and forth.

3) For most frequencies the resultant **pattern** is a **jumble**. However, if the oscillator happens to produce an **exact number of waves** in the time it takes for a wave to get to the **end** and **back again**, then the **original** and **reflected** waves **reinforce** each other.

4) At these **"resonant frequencies"** you get a **standing wave** where the **pattern doesn't move** — it just sits there, bobbing up and down. Happy, at peace with the world...

A sitting wave.

Standing Waves in **Strings** Form **Oscillating "Loops"** Separated by **Nodes**

1) Each particle vibrates at **right angles** to the string.
   Nodes are where the **amplitude** of the vibration is **zero**.
   Antinodes are points of **maximum amplitude**.

2) At resonant frequencies, an **exact number** of **half wavelengths** fits onto the string.

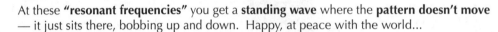

The standing wave above is vibrating at the **lowest possible** resonant frequency (the **fundamental frequency**). It has **one** "loop" with a **node at each end**.

This is the **second harmonic** (or **first overtone**). It is **twice** the fundamental frequency. There are two "loops" with a **node** in the **middle** and **one at each end**.

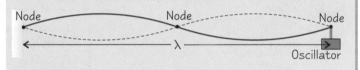

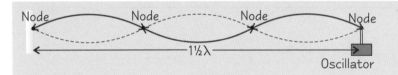

The **third harmonic** (or **second overtone**) is **three times** the fundamental frequency. **1½ wavelengths** fit on the string.

The **Notes** Played by **Stringed** and **Wind Instruments** are Standing Waves

Transverse standing waves form on the strings of **stringed instruments** like **violins** and **guitars**. Your finger or the bow sets the **string vibrating** at the point of contact. Waves are sent out in **both directions** and **reflected** back at both ends.

Longitudinal Standing Waves Form in a **Wind Instrument** or Other **Air Column**

1) If a source of sound is placed at the open end of a flute, piccolo, oboe or other column of air, there will be some **frequencies** for which **resonance** occurs and a standing wave is set up.

2) If the instrument has a **closed end**, a **node** will form there. You get the lowest resonant frequency when the length, *l*, of the pipe is a **quarter wavelength**.

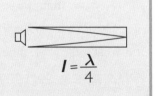

$$l = \frac{\lambda}{4}$$

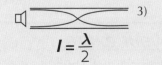

$$l = \frac{\lambda}{2}$$

3) **Antinodes** form at the **open ends** of pipes. If both ends are open, you get the lowest resonant frequency when the length, *l*, of the pipe is a **half wavelength**.

Remember, the sound waves in wind instruments are <u>longitudinal</u> — they <u>don't</u> actually look like these diagrams.

Stationary (Standing) Waves

You can Demonstrate Standing Waves with Microwaves

Microwaves Reflected Off a Metal Plate Set Up a Standing Wave

Microwave standing wave apparatus ➡
You can find the **nodes** and **antinodes** by moving the **probe** between the **transmitter** and the **reflecting** plate.

metal plate

microwave transmitter

probe

to meter or loudspeaker

You can Use Standing Waves to Measure the Speed of Sound

OCR A only

Finding the Speed of Sound in a Resonance Tube

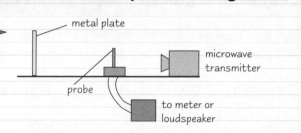

tuning fork

$\frac{\lambda}{4}$

node

water

measuring cylinder

hollow plastic tube

1) You can create a closed-end pipe by placing a **hollow tube** into a measuring cylinder of water.

2) Choose a tuning fork and note down the frequency of sound it produces (it'll be stamped on the side of it).

3) Gently tap the tuning fork and hold it just above the hollow tube. The sound waves produced by the fork travel down the tube and get reflected (and form a **node**) at the air/water surface.

4) Move the tube up and down until you find the **shortest distance** between the top of the tube and the water level that the sound from the fork **resonates** at.

5) Just like with any closed pipe, this distance is a **quarter** of the **wavelength** of the standing sound wave.

6) The antinode of the wave actually forms slightly **above** the top of the tube — so you need to add a constant called an **end correction** to the length of your tube **before** you can work out the wavelength.

7) Once you know the **frequency** and **wavelength** of the standing sound wave, you can work out the **speed of sound** (in air), v, using the equation $v = f\lambda$.

Practice Questions

Q1 How do standing waves form?

Q2 At four times the fundamental frequency, how many half wavelengths fit on a violin string?

Q3 Describe an experiment to find the speed of sound in air using standing waves.

Exam Question

Q1 (a) A standing wave of three times the fundamental frequency is formed on a stretched string of length 1.2 m. Sketch a diagram showing the form of the wave. [2 marks]

(b) What is the wavelength of the standing wave? [1 mark]

(c) Explain how the amplitude varies along the string. How is that different from the amplitude of a progressive wave? [2 marks]

CGP — putting the FUN back in FUNdamental frequency...

Resonance was a big problem for the Millennium Bridge in London. The resonant frequency of the bridge was round about normal walking pace, so as soon as people started using it they set up a huge standing wave. An oversight, I feel...

Diffraction

These pages are for AQA A Unit 2, Edexcel Unit 2, OCR A Unit 2 and OCR B Unit 2.

Ripple tanks, ripple tanks — yeah.

Waves Go **Round Corners** and **Spread out** of **Gaps**

The way that **waves spread out** as they come through a **narrow gap** or go round obstacles is called **diffraction**.   **All** waves diffract, but it's not always easy to observe.

Use a **Ripple Tank** To Show Diffraction of **Water Waves**
You can make diffraction patterns in ripple tanks.
The **amount** of diffraction depends on the **wavelength** of the wave compared with the **size of the gap**.

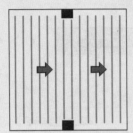 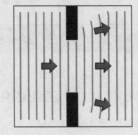 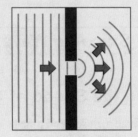

When the gap is **a lot bigger** than the **wavelength**, diffraction is **unnoticeable**.

You get **noticeable diffraction** through a gap **several** wavelengths wide.

You get the **most** diffraction when the gap is **the same** size as the **wavelength**.

If the gap is **smaller** than the wavelength, the waves are mostly just **reflected back**.

When **sound** passes through a **doorway**, the **size of gap** and the **wavelength** are usually roughly **equal**, so **a lot** of **diffraction** occurs. That's why you have no trouble **hearing** someone through an **open door** to the next room, even if the other person is out of your **line of sight**. The reason that you can't **see** him or her is that when **light** passes through the doorway, it is passing through a **gap** around a **hundred million times bigger** than its wavelength — the amount of diffraction is **tiny**.

Demonstrate **Diffraction** in **Light** Using **Laser Light**
1) Diffraction in **light** can be demonstrated by shining a **laser light** through a very **narrow slit** onto a screen (see page 85). You can alter the amount of diffraction by changing the width of the slit.

2) You can do a similar experiment using a **white light** source instead of the laser (which is monochromatic) and a set of **colour filters**. The size of the slit can be kept constant while the **wavelength** is varied by putting different **colour filters** over the slit.

Warning. Use of coloured filters may result in excessive fun.

*You Get a **Similar** Effect Around an **Obstacle***

When a wave meets an **obstacle**, you get diffraction around the edges.

Behind the obstacle is a '**shadow**', where the wave is blocked. The **wider** the obstacle compared with the wavelength of the wave, the less diffraction you get, and so the **longer** the shadow.

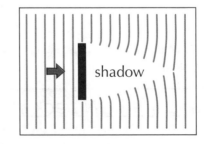

Diffraction

With Light Waves you get a Pattern of Light and Dark Fringes

1) If the **wavelength** of a **light wave** is about the same size as the **aperture**, you get a **diffraction pattern** of light and dark fringes.

2) The pattern has a **bright central fringe** with alternating **dark and bright fringes** on either side of it.

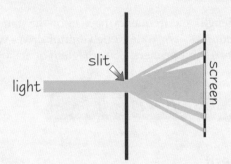
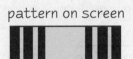

You need to use a coherent light source for this experiment.

3) The **narrower** the slit, the **wider** the diffraction pattern.

You Get a Similar Pattern with Electrons

1) It's not just with **light** that you get diffraction patterns.

2) In **1927**, two American physicists, **Clinton Davisson** and **Lester Germer**, succeeded in diffracting **electrons**.

3) This was a **huge** discovery. A few years earlier, **Louis de Broglie** had **hypothesised** that electrons would show **wave-like** properties (in the same way that light can show particle-like properties — more about that in Section Six), but this was the first **direct evidence** for it.

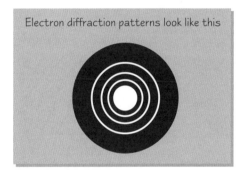
Electron diffraction patterns look like this

Practice Questions

Q1 What is diffraction?

Q2 Sketch what happens when plane waves meet an obstacle about as wide as one wavelength.

Q3 For a long time some scientists argued that light couldn't be a wave because it did not seem to diffract. Suggest why they might have got this impression.

Q4 Do all waves diffract?

Exam Question

Q1 A mountain lies directly between you and a radio transmitter.

Explain using diagrams why you can pick up long-wave radio broadcasts from the transmitter but not short-wave radio broadcasts. [4 marks]

Even hiding behind a mountain, you can't get away from long-wave radio...

*Unfortunately "Bay fm" don't transmit using long wave radio. So as I'm giving the singing-in-the-car performance of my life, I go over a hill and the signal cuts out. Where's diffraction when I need it then hmm? Diffraction crops up again in particle physics, quantum physics and astronomy, so make sure you **really** need to understand it.*

Two-Source Interference

These pages are for AQA A Unit 2, OCR A Unit 2 and OCR B Unit 2.

Yeah, I know, fringe spacing doesn't really sound like a Physics topic — just trust me on this one, OK.

Demonstrating Two-Source Interference in *Water* and *Sound* is Easy

1) It's **easy** to demonstrate **two-source interference** for either **sound** or **water** because they've got **wavelengths** of a handy **size** that you can **measure**.

2) You need **coherent** sources, which means the **wavelength** and **frequency** have to be the **same**. The trick is to use the **same oscillator** to drive **both sources**. For **water**, one vibrator drives two **dippers**. For sound, **one oscillator** is connected to **two loudspeakers**. (See diagram on page 81.)

Demonstrating *Two-Source* Interference for *Light* is Harder

Young's Double-Slit Experiment

1) You **can't** arrange **two separate coherent light sources** because **light** from **each source** is emitted in **random bursts**. Instead a **single** laser is shone through **two slits**.

2) Laser light is **coherent** and **monochromatic** (there's only **one wavelength** present).

3) The slits have to be narrower than the wavelength of the laser light so that it is **diffracted** — then the light from the slits is equivalent to **two coherent point sources**.

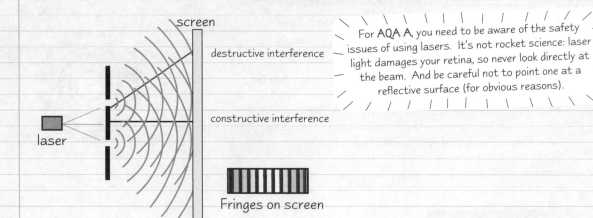

For AQA A, you need to be aware of the safety issues of using lasers. It's not rocket science: laser light damages your retina, so never look directly at the beam. And be careful not to point one at a reflective surface (for obvious reasons).

4) You get a pattern of light and dark **fringes**, depending on whether constructive or destructive **interference** is taking place. Thomas Young — the first person to do this experiment (with a lamp rather than a laser) — came up with an **equation** to **work out** the **wavelength** of the **light** from this experiment (see next page).

You Can Do a *Similar* Experiment with *Microwaves*

1) To see interference patterns with **microwaves**, you can **replace** the laser and slits with two microwave **transmitter cones** attached to the **same** signal generator.

2) You also need to replace the screen with a microwave **receiver probe** (like the one used in the standing waves experiment on page 83).

3) If you move the probe along the path of the green arrow, you'll get an **alternating pattern** of **strong** and **weak** signals — just like the light and dark fringes on the screen.

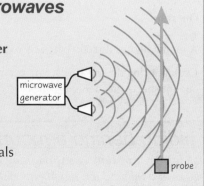

Two-Source Interference

Work Out the Wavelength with Young's Double-Slit Formula

1) The fringe spacing (**X**), wavelength (**λ**), spacing between slits (**d**) and the distance from slits to screen (**D**) are all related by **Young's double-slit formula**, which works for all waves (you need to know it, but not derive it).

$$\text{Fringe spacing}, X = \frac{D\lambda}{d}$$

"Fringe spacing" means the distance from the centre of one minimum to the centre of the next minimum or from the centre of one maximum to the centre of the next maximum.

2) Since the wavelength of light is so small you can see from the formula that a high ratio of **D / d** is needed to make the fringe spacing **big enough to see**.

3) Rearranging, you can use **λ = Xd / D** to **calculate the wavelength** of light.

4) The fringes are **so tiny** that it's very hard to get an **accurate value of X**. It's easier to measure across **several** fringes then **divide** by the number of **fringe widths** between them.

Always check your fringe spacing.

Young's Experiment was Evidence for the Wave Nature of Light

1) Towards the end of the **17th century**, two important **theories of light** were published — one by Isaac Newton and the other by a chap called Huygens. **Newton's** theory suggested that light was made up of tiny particles, which he called "**corpuscles**". And **Huygens** put forward a theory using **waves**.

2) The **corpuscular theory** could explain **reflection and refraction**, but **diffraction** and **interference** are both **uniquely** wave properties. If it could be **shown** that light showed interference patterns, that would help settle the argument once and for all.

3) **Young's** double-slit experiment (over 100 years later) provided the necessary evidence. It showed that light could both **diffract** (through the narrow slits) and **interfere** (to form the interference pattern on the screen).

Of course, this being Physics, nothing's ever simple — give it another 100 years or so and the debate would be raging again. But that can wait for Section Six...

Practice Questions

Q1 In Young's experiment, why do you get a bright fringe at a point equidistant from both slits?

Q2 What does Young's experiment show about the nature of light?

Q3 Write down Young's double-slit formula.

Exam Questions

Q1 (a) The diagram on the right shows waves from two coherent light sources, S_1 and S_2. Sketch the interference pattern, marking on constructive and destructive interference. [2 marks]

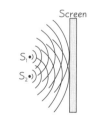

(b) In practice if interference is to be observed, S_1 and S_2 must be slits in a screen behind which there is a source of laser light. Why? [2 marks]

Q2 In an experiment to study sound interference, two loudspeakers are connected to an oscillator emitting sound at 1320 Hz and set up as shown in the diagram below. They are 1.5 m apart and 7 m away from the line AC. A listener moving from A to C hears minimum sound at A and C and maximum sound at B.

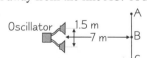

(a) Calculate the wavelength of the sound waves if the speed of sound in air is taken to be 330 ms⁻¹. [1 mark]

(b) Calculate the separation of points A and C. [2 marks]

Carry on Physics — this page is far too saucy...

Be careful when you're calculating the fringe width by averaging over several fringes. Don't just divide by the number of bright lines. Ten bright lines will only have nine fringe-widths between them, not ten. It's an easy mistake to make, but you have been warned... mwa ha ha ha (felt necessary, sorry).

* *Sadly, Barbara Windsor was unavailable.*

Diffraction Gratings

These pages are for AQA A Unit 2, OCR A Unit 2 and OCR B Unit 2.

Ay... starting to get into some pretty funky stuff now. I like light experiments.

Interference Patterns Get **Sharper** When You Diffract Through **More Slits**

1) You can repeat **Young's double-slit** experiment (see p. 86) with **more than two equally spaced** slits. You get basically the **same shaped** pattern as for two slits — but the **bright bands** are **brighter** and **narrower** and the **dark areas** between are **darker**.

2) When **monochromatic light** (one wavelength) is passed through a **grating** with **hundreds** of slits per millimetre, the interference pattern is **really sharp** because there are so **many beams reinforcing** the **pattern**.

3) Sharper fringes make for more **accurate** measurements.

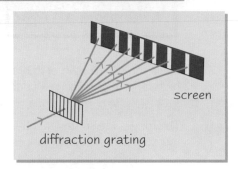

Monochromatic Light on a **Diffraction Grating** gives **Sharp Lines**

1) For **monochromatic** light, all the **maxima** are sharp lines. (It's different for white light — see next page.)

2) There's a line of **maximum brightness** at the centre called the **zero order** line.

3) The lines just **either side** of the central one are called **first order lines**. The **next pair out** are called **second order** lines and so on.

4) For a grating with slits a distance *d* apart, the angle between the **incident beam** and **the nth order maximum** is given by:

$$d \sin \theta = n\lambda$$

5) So by observing *d*, *θ* and *n* you can **calculate the wavelength** of the light.

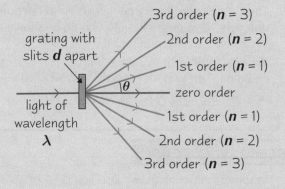

If the grating has N slits per metre, then the slit spacing, d, is just 1/N metres.

DERIVING THE EQUATION: *AQA A only*

1) At **each slit**, the incoming waves are **diffracted**. These diffracted waves then **interfere** with each other to produce an **interference pattern**.

2) Consider the **first order maximum**. This happens at the **angle** when the waves from one slit line up with waves from the **next slit** that are **exactly one wavelength** behind.

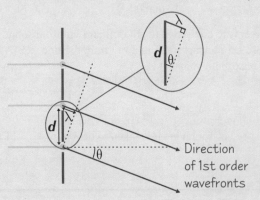

3) Call the **angle** between the **first order maximum** and the **incoming light** θ.

4) Now, look at the **triangle** highlighted in the diagram. The angle is θ (using basic geometry), *d* is the slit spacing and the **path difference** is λ.

5) So, for the first maximum, using trig:
$$d \sin \theta = \lambda$$

6) The other maxima occur when the path difference is 2λ, 3λ, 4λ, etc. So to make the equation **general**, just replace λ with *n*λ, where *n* is an integer — the **order** of the maximum.

Diffraction Gratings

You can Draw **General Conclusions** from **d sin θ = nλ**

1) If λ is **bigger**, sin θ is **bigger**, and so θ is **bigger**. This means that the larger the **wavelength**, the more the pattern will **spread out**.

2) If d is **bigger**, sin θ is **smaller**. This means that the **coarser** the grating, the **less** the pattern will **spread out**.

3) Values of sin θ greater than **1** are **impossible**. So if for a certain n you get a result of **more than 1** for sin θ you know that that order **doesn't exist**.

Shining **White Light** Through a **Diffraction Grating** Produces **Spectra**

1) **White light** is really a **mixture** of **colours**. If you **diffract** white light through a **grating** then the patterns due to **different wavelengths** within the white light are **spread out** by **different** amounts.

2) Each **order** in the pattern becomes a **spectrum**, with **red** on the **outside** and **violet** on the **inside**. The **zero order maximum** stays **white** because all the wavelengths just pass straight through.

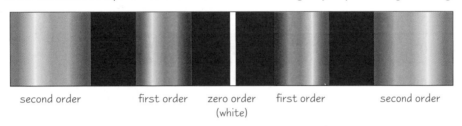

second order   first order   zero order   first order   second order
(white)

Astronomers and **chemists** often need to study spectra to help identify elements. They use diffraction gratings rather than prisms because they're **more accurate**.

Practice Questions

Q1 How is the diffraction grating pattern for white light different from the pattern for laser light?

Q2 What difference does it make to the pattern if you use a finer grating?

Q3 What equation is used to find the angle between the nth order maximum and the incident beam for a diffraction grating?

Q4 Derive the equation you quoted in Q3.

Exam Questions

Q1 Yellow laser light of wavelength 600 nm (6×10^{-7} m) is transmitted through a diffraction grating of 4×10^5 lines per metre.

(a) At what angle to the normal are the first and second order bright lines seen? [4 marks]

(b) Is there a fifth order line? [1 mark]

Q2 Visible, monochromatic light is transmitted through a diffraction grating of 3.7×10^5 lines per metre. The first order maximum is at an angle of 14.2° to the incident beam.

Find the wavelength of the incident light. [2 marks]

Oooooooooooooo — pretty patterns...

*Derivation — ouch. At least it's not a bad one though. As long as you learn the diagram, its just geometry and a bit of trig from there. Make sure you **learn** the equation — that way, you know what you're aiming for. As for the rest of the page, remember that the more slits you have, the sharper the image — and white light makes a pretty spectrum.*

Light — Wave or Particle

These pages are for AQA A Unit 1, Edexcel Unit 2, OCR A Unit 2 and OCR B Unit 2.

You probably already thought light was a bit weird — but oh no... being a wave that travels at the fastest speed possible isn't enough for light — it has to go one step further and act like a particle too...

Light *Travels at* High Speed

1)   Light travels really quickly — around **3.00 × 10⁸ ms⁻¹**.

2)   And that makes its speed really hard to measure.
You only really notice that light takes **time** to travel anywhere if it's travelling over a **very large distance** (like in astronomy), or if you've got a really accurate clock.
(There's also a rather clever method for measuring its speed using interference, but you don't need to know about that.)

> **Example**   Light takes roughly 1.25 seconds to travel from the Moon to the Earth. The Moon's average distance from the Earth is 3.8×10^8 m. Find the speed of light, *c*.
>
> Speed of light, $c = 3.8 \times 10^8 \div 1.25 = 3.0 \times 10^8$ ms⁻¹ (to 2 s.f.)

Light might be faster, but Sheila doubted it could look quite as fetching in shorts

Light Behaves Like a *Wave*... or a *Stream of Particles*

1)   In the **late nineteenth century**, if you asked what light was, scientists would happily show you lots of nice experiments showing how light must be a **wave** (see Section 5).

2)   Then came the **photoelectric effect** (p. 92), which mucked up everything.
The only way you could explain this effect was if light acted as a **particle** — called a **photon**.

A *Photon* is a *Quantum* of *EM Radiation*

1)   When Max Planck was investigating **black body radiation** (don't worry — you don't need to know about that just yet), he suggested that **EM waves** can **only** be **released** in **discrete packets**, called **quanta.** A single packet of **EM radiation** is called a **quantum**.

The **energy carried** by one of these **wave-packets** had to be:

$$E = hf = \frac{hc}{\lambda}$$

where h = Planck's constant = 6.63×10^{-34} Js,
f = frequency (Hz), λ = wavelength (m)
and c = speed of light in a vacuum = 3.00×10^8 ms⁻¹

2)   So, the **higher** the **frequency** of the electromagnetic radiation, the more **energy** its wave-packets carry.

3)   **Einstein** went **further** by suggesting that **EM waves** (and the energy they carry) can only **exist** in discrete packets. He called these wave-packets **photons**.

4)   He believed that a photon acts as **particle**, and will either transfer **all** or **none** of its energy when interacting with another particle, like an electron.

Photon Energies *are Usually Given in* Electronvolts

1)   The **energies involved** when you're talking about photons are **so tiny** that it makes sense to use a more **appropriate unit** than the **joule**. Bring on the **electronvolt** ...

2)   When you **accelerate** an electron between two electrodes, it transfers some electrical potential energy (eV) into kinetic energy.

$$eV = \frac{1}{2}mv^2$$

e is the charge on an electron: 1.6×10^{-19} C.

3)   An electronvolt is defined as:

> The **kinetic energy gained** by an **electron** when it is **accelerated** through a **potential difference** of **1 volt**.

4)   So 1 electron volt = $e \times V = 1.6 \times 10^{-19}$ C × 1 JC⁻¹.   ⟹ $\boxed{1 \text{ eV} = 1.6 \times 10^{-19} \text{ J}}$

Light — Wave or Particle

You can Use *LEDs* to *Calculate Planck's Constant*

OCR A only

1) Planck's constant comes up everywhere — but it's not just some random number plucked out of the air. You can find its value by doing a simple experiment with **light-emitting diodes** (**LED**s).

2) Current will only pass through an LED after a **minimum voltage** is placed across it — the **threshold voltage V_0**.

3) This is the voltage needed to give the electrons the **same energy** as a photon emitted by the LED. **All** of the electron's **kinetic energy** after it is accelerated over this potential difference is **transferred** into a **photon**.

$$E = \frac{hc}{\lambda} = eV_0 \Rightarrow h = \frac{(eV_0)\lambda}{c}$$

4) So by finding the threshold voltage for a particular wavelength LED, you can calculate Planck's constant.

Experiment to Measure Planck's Constant

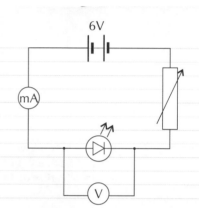

1) Connect an LED of known wavelength in the electrical circuit shown.

2) Start off with no current flowing through the circuit, then adjust the variable resistor until a current just begins to flow through the circuit.

3) Record the voltage (V_0) across the LED, and the wavelength of light the LED emits.

4) Repeat this experiment with a number of LEDs that emit different optical wavelengths.

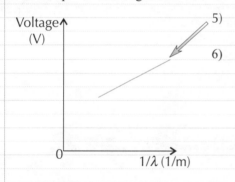

5) Plot a graph of threshold voltages (V_0) against $1/\lambda$ (where λ is the wavelength of light emitted by the LED in metres).

6) You should get a straight line graph with a gradient of hc/e — which you can then use to find the value of h.

E.g.
$$\text{gradient} = \frac{hc}{e} = 1.24 \times 10^{-6},$$

$$\text{so } h = \frac{1.24 \times 10^{-6} e}{c} = \frac{(1.24 \times 10^{-6}) \times (1.6 \times 10^{-19})}{3 \times 10^8}$$

$$= 6.6 \times 10^{-34} \text{ Js (2 s.f.)}$$

Practice Questions

Q1 Give two different ways to describe the nature of light.

Q2 Write down the two formulae you can use to find the energy of a photon. Include the meanings of all the symbols you use.

Q3 What is an electronvolt? What is 1 eV in joules?

Exam Question

Q1 An LED is tested and found to have a threshold voltage of 1.70 V.

(a) Find the energy of the photons emitted by the LED. Give your answer in joules. [2 marks]

(b) The LED emits light with a wavelength of 700 nm.
Use your answer from a) to calculate the value of Planck's constant. [2 marks]
($c = 3.0 \times 10^{-8} \text{ ms}^{-1}$)

Millions of light particles are hitting your retinas as you read this... PANIC...

I hate it in physics when they tell you lies, make you learn it, and just when you've got to grips with it they tell you it was all a load of codswallop. This is the real deal folks — light isn't just the nice wave you've always known...

The Photoelectric Effect

These pages are for AQA A Unit 1, Edexcel Unit 2, OCR A Unit 2 and OCR B Unit 2.

The photoelectric effect was one of the original troublemakers in the light-is-it-a-wave-or-a-particle problem...

Shining Light on a Metal can Release Electrons

If you shine **light** of a **high enough frequency** onto the **surface of a metal**,
it will **emit electrons**. For **most** metals, this **frequency** falls in the **U.V.** range.

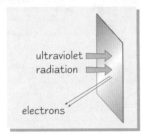

ultraviolet
radiation

electrons

1) **Free electrons** on the **surface** of the metal **absorb energy**
    from the light, making them **vibrate**.

2) If an electron **absorbs enough** energy, the **bonds** holding
    it to the metal **break** and the electron is **released**.

3) This is called the **photoelectric effect** and the electrons
    emitted are called **photoelectrons**.

You don't need to know the details of any experiments on this — you just need to learn the three main conclusions:

Conclusion 1	For a given metal, **no photoelectrons are emitted** if the radiation has a frequency **below** a certain value — called the **threshold frequency**.
Conclusion 2	The photoelectrons are emitted with a variety of kinetic energies ranging from zero to some maximum value. This value of **maximum kinetic energy** increases with the **frequency** of the radiation, and is **unaffected** by the **intensity** of the radiation.
Conclusion 3	The **number** of photoelectrons emitted per second is **proportional** to the **intensity** of the radiation.

These are the two that had scientists puzzled. They can't be explained using wave theory.

The Photoelectric Effect Couldn't be Explained by Wave Theory

According to wave theory:

1) For a particular frequency of light, the **energy** carried is **proportional** to the **intensity** of the beam.

2) The energy carried by the light would be **spread evenly** over the wavefront.

3) **Each** free electron on the surface of the metal would gain a **bit of energy** from each incoming wave.

4) Gradually, each electron would gain **enough energy** to leave the metal.

SO... If the light had a **lower frequency** (i.e. was carrying less energy) it would take **longer** for the electrons to gain
enough energy — but it would happen eventually. There is **no explanation** for the **threshold frequency**.

The **higher the intensity** of the wave, the **more energy** it should transfer to each electron — the kinetic energy
should increase with **intensity**. There's **no explanation** for the **kinetic energy** depending only on the **frequency**.

The Photon Model Explained the Photoelectric Effect Nicely

According to the photon model (see page 90)**:**

1) When light hits its surface, the metal is **bombarded** by photons.

2) If one of these photons **collides** with a free electron, the electron will gain energy equal to *hf*.

Before an electron can **leave** the surface of the metal, it needs enough energy to **break the bonds holding it there**.
This energy is called the **work function energy** (symbol ϕ (phi)) and its **value** depends on the **metal**.

The Photoelectric Effect

It Explains the Threshold Frequency...

1) If the energy **gained** from the photon is **greater** than the **work function energy**, the electron can be **emitted**.

2) If it **isn't**, the electron will just **shake about a bit**, then release the energy as another photon. The metal will heat up, but **no electrons** will be emitted.

3) Since for **electrons** to be released, $hf \geq \phi$, the **threshold frequency** must be:

$$f = \frac{\phi}{h}$$

In theory, if a second photon hit an electron before it released the energy from the first, it could gain enough to leave the metal. This would have to happen very quickly though. An electron releases any excess energy after about 10^{-8} s. That's 0.000 000 01 s — safe to say, the chances of that happening are pretty slim.

... and the Maximum Kinetic Energy

1) The **energy transferred** to an electron is **hf**.

2) The **kinetic energy** it will be carrying when it **leaves** the metal will be h*f* **minus** any energy it's **lost** on the way out (there are loads of ways it can do that, which explains the **range** of energies).

3) The **minimum** amount of energy it can lose is the **work function energy**, so the **maximum kinetic energy** is given by the equation:

$$hf = \phi + \frac{1}{2}mv_{max}^2$$

4) The **kinetic energy** of the electrons is **independent of the intensity**, because they can **only absorb one photon** at a time.

Practice Questions

Q1 Describe an experiment that demonstrates the photoelectric effect.

Q2 What is meant by the threshold frequency?

Q3 Write down the equation that relates the work function of a metal and the threshold frequency.

Q4 Write an equation that relates the maximum kinetic energy of a photoelectron released from a metal surface and the frequency of the incident light on the surface.

Exam Questions

Planck's constant, $h = 6.63 \times 10^{-34}$ Js

Q1 The work function of calcium is 2.9 eV.
Find the threshold frequency of radiation needed for the photoelectric effect to take place. [2 marks]

Q2 The surface of a copper plate is illuminated with monochromatic ultraviolet light, with a frequency of 2.0×10^{15} Hz. The work function for copper is 4.7 eV.
(a) Find the energy in eV carried by one ultraviolet photon. [3 marks]
(b) Find the maximum kinetic energy of a photoelectron emitted from the copper surface. [2 marks]

Q3 Explain why the photoelectric effect only occurs after the incident light has reached a certain frequency. [2 marks]

I'm so glad we got that all cleared up...

Well, that's about as hard as it gets at AS. The most important bits here are why wave theory doesn't explain the phenomenon, and why the photon theory does. A good way to learn conceptual stuff like this is to try to explain it to someone else. You'll get the formulae in your handy data book, but it's probably a good idea to learn them too...

Energy Levels and Photon Emission

These pages are for AQA A Unit 1, Edexcel Unit 2, OCR A Unit 2 and OCR B Unit 2.

Electrons in Atoms Exist in Discrete Energy Levels

1) **Electrons** in an **atom** can **only exist** in certain **well-defined energy levels**. Each level is given a **number**, with **n = 1** representing the **ground state**.

2) Electrons can **move down** an energy level by **emitting** a **photon**.

3) Since these **transitions** are between **definite energy levels**, the **energy** of **each photon** emitted can **only** take a **certain allowed value**.

4) The diagram on the right shows the **energy levels** for **atomic hydrogen**.

5) On the diagram, energies are labelled in both **joules** and **electonvolts** for **comparison's** sake.

6) The **energy** carried by each **photon** is **equal** to the **difference in energies** between the **two levels**. The equation below shows a **transition** between levels **n = 2** and **n = 1**:

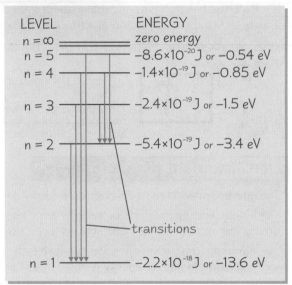

LEVEL	ENERGY
$n = \infty$	zero energy
$n = 5$	-8.6×10^{-20} J or -0.54 eV
$n = 4$	-1.4×10^{-19} J or -0.85 eV
$n = 3$	-2.4×10^{-19} J or -1.5 eV
$n = 2$	-5.4×10^{-19} J or -3.4 eV
$n = 1$	-2.2×10^{-18} J or -13.6 eV

transitions

$$\Delta E = E_2 - E_1 = hf = \frac{hc}{\lambda}$$

The energies are only negative because of how "zero energy" is defined. Just one of those silly convention things — don't worry about it.

Fluorescent Tubes use Excited Electrons to Produce Light   *AQA A only*

1) **Fluorescent tubes** contain **mercury vapour**, across which a **high voltage** is applied.

2) When **electrons** in the **mercury collide** with **fast-moving free electrons** (accelerated by the **high voltage**), they're **excited** to a **higher energy level**.

3) When these **excited electrons** return to their **ground states**, they emit **photons** in the **UV** range.

4) A **phosphorus coating** on the **inside** of the tube **absorbs** these **photons**, exciting its **electrons** to **much higher orbits**. These electrons then **cascade** down the **energy levels**, **emitting** many **lower energy photons** in the form of **visible light**.

Fluorescent Tubes Produce Line Emission Spectra

1) If you **split** the light from a **fluorescent tube** with a **prism** or a **diffraction grating** (see pages 88-89), you get a **line spectrum**.

2) A line spectrum is seen as a **series** of **bright lines** against a **black background**.

3) Each **line** corresponds to a **particular wavelength** of light **emitted** by the source.

4) Since only **certain photon energies** are **allowed**, you only see the **corresponding wavelengths**.

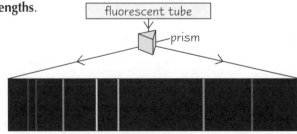

fluorescent tube

prism

Energy Levels and Photon Emission

The rest of this is for OCR A Unit 2 only

Shining **White Light** through a **Cool Gas** gives an **Absorption Spectrum**

Continuous Spectra Contain **All** Possible **Wavelengths**

1) The **spectrum** of **white light** is **continuous**.

2) If you **split** the **light** up with a **prism**, the **colours** all **merge** into each other — there **aren't** any **gaps** in the spectrum.

3) **Hot things** emit a **continuous spectrum** in the visible and infrared.

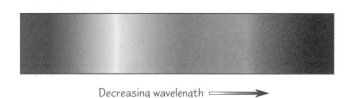

Decreasing wavelength ⟹

Cool Gases **Remove** Certain **Wavelengths** from the Continuous Spectrum

1) You get a **line absorption spectrum** when **light** with a **continuous spectrum** of **energy** (white light) passes through a cool gas.

2) At **low temperatures**, **most** of the **electrons** in the **gas atoms** will be in their **ground states**.

3) **Photons** of the **correct wavelength** are **absorbed** by the **electrons** to **excite** them to **higher energy levels**.

4) These **wavelengths** are then **missing** from the **continuous spectrum** when it **comes out** the other side of the gas.

5) You see a **continuous spectrum** with **black lines** in it corresponding to the **absorbed wavelengths**.

6) If you **compare** the **absorption** and **emission** spectra of a **particular gas**, the **black lines** in the **absorption spectrum match up** to the **bright lines** in the **emission spectrum**.

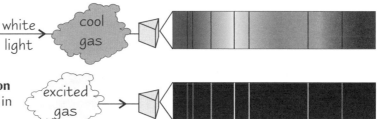

Practice Questions

Q1 Describe line absorption and line emission spectra. How are these two types of spectra produced?

Q2 Use the size of the energy level transitions involved to explain how the coating on a fluorescent tube converts UV into visible light.

Exam Question

Q1 An electron is accelerated through a potential difference of 12.1 V.
($e = -1.6 \times 10^{-19}$ C)

(a) How much kinetic energy has it gained in (i) eV and (ii) joules? [1 mark]

(b) This electron hits a hydrogen atom and excites it.
    (i) Explain what is meant by excitation. [1 mark]
    (ii) Using the energy values on the right, work out to which energy level the electron from the hydrogen atom is excited. [1 mark]
    (iii) Calculate the energies of the three photons that might be emitted as the electron returns to its ground state. [3 marks]

n = 5	− 0.54 eV
n = 4	− 0.85 eV
n = 3	− 1.5 eV
n = 2	− 3.4 eV
n = 1	− 13.6 eV

I can honestly say I've never got so excited that I've produced light...

This is heavy stuff, it really is. Quite interesting though, as I was just saying to Dom a moment ago. He's doing a psychology book. Psychology's probably quite interesting too — and easier. But it won't help you become an astrophysicist.

Wave-Particle Duality

These pages are for AQA A Unit 1, Edexcel Unit 2 and OCR A Unit 2.

Is it a wave? Is it a particle? No, it's a wave. No, it's a particle. No it's not, it's a wave. No don't be daft, it's a particle. (etc.)

Interference and Diffraction show Light as a Wave

1) Light produces **interference** and **diffraction** patterns — **alternating bands** of **dark** and **light**.
2) These can **only** be explained using **waves interfering constructively** (when two waves overlap in phase) or **interfering destructively** (when the two waves are out of phase). (See p.81.)

The Photoelectric Effect Shows Light Behaving as a Particle

1) **Einstein** explained the results of **photoelectricity experiments** (see p.92) by thinking of the **beam of light** as a series of **particle-like photons**.
2) If a **photon** of light is a **discrete** bundle of energy, then it can **interact** with an **electron** in a **one-to-one way**.
3) **All** the **energy** in the **photon** is **given** to one **electron**.

De Broglie Came up With the Wave-Particle Duality Theory

1) Louis de Broglie made a **bold suggestion** in his **PhD thesis**:

   If 'wave-like' **light** showed **particle properties** (photons), 'particles' like **electrons** should be expected to show **wave-like properties**.

2) The **de Broglie equation** relates a **wave property** (**wavelength**, λ) to a **moving particle property** (**momentum**, *mv*). *h* = Planck's constant = 6.63×10^{-34} Js.

$$\lambda = \frac{h}{mv}$$

3) The **de Broglie wave** of a particle can be interpreted as a '**probability wave**'. (The probability of finding a particle at a point is directly proportional to the square of the amplitude of the wave at that point — but you don't need to know that for your exam.)
4) Many physicists at the time **weren't very impressed** — his ideas were just **speculation**. But later experiments **confirmed** the wave nature of electrons.

I'm not impressed — this is just speculation. What do you think Dad?

Electron Diffraction shows the Wave Nature of Electrons

1) **Diffraction patterns** are observed when **accelerated electrons** in a vacuum tube **interact** with the **spaces** in a graphite **crystal**.
2) This **confirms** that electrons show **wave-like** properties.
3) According to wave theory, the **spread** of the **lines** in the diffraction pattern **increases** if the **wavelength** of the wave is **greater**.
4) In electron diffraction experiments, a **smaller accelerating voltage**, i.e. **slower** electrons, gives **widely spaced** rings.
5) **Increase** the **electron speed** and the diffraction pattern circles **squash together** towards the **middle**. This fits in with the **de Broglie** equation above — if the **velocity** is **higher**, the **wavelength** is **shorter** and the **spread** of lines is **smaller**.

   In general, λ for **electrons** accelerated in a **vacuum tube** is about the **same size** as **electromagnetic waves** in the **X-ray** part of the spectrum.

Wave-Particle Duality

Particles Don't show Wave-Like Properties All the Time

You **only** get **diffraction** if a particle interacts with an object of about the **same size** as its **de Broglie wavelength**.
A **tennis ball**, for example, with **mass 0.058 kg** and **speed 100 ms⁻¹** has a **de Broglie wavelength** of **10⁻³⁴ m**.
That's **10¹⁹ times smaller** than the **nucleus** of an **atom**! There's nothing that small for it to interact with.

> *Example*   An electron of mass 9.11×10^{-31} kg is fired from an electron gun at 7×10^6 ms⁻¹.
> What size object will the electron need to interact with in order to diffract?
>
> Momentum of electron = mv = 6.38×10^{-24} kg ms⁻¹
> $\lambda = h/mv = 6.63 \times 10^{-34} / 6.38 \times 10^{-24} = \boxed{1 \times 10^{-10} \text{ m}}$
>
> Only crystals with atom layer spacing around this size are likely to cause the diffraction of this electron.

A **shorter wavelength** gives **less diffraction effects**. This fact is used in the **electron microscope**.
Diffraction effects **blur detail** on an image. If you want to **resolve tiny detail** in an **image**, you need a **shorter wavelength**. **Light** blurs out detail more than 'electron-waves' do, so an **electron microscope** can resolve **finer detail** than a **light microscope**. They can let you look at things as tiny as a single strand of DNA... which is nice.

Practice Questions

Q1   Which observations show light to have a 'wave-like' character?

Q2   Which observations show light to have a 'particle' character?

Q3   What happens to the de Broglie wavelength of a particle if its velocity increases?

Q4   Which observations show electrons to have a 'wave-like' character?

Exam Questions

$h = 6.63 \times 10^{-34}$ Js ; $c = 3.00 \times 10^8$ ms⁻¹ ; electron mass = 9.11×10^{-31} kg ; proton mass = $1840 \times$ electron mass

Q1   (a) State what is meant by the wave-particle duality of electromagnetic radiation.   [1 mark]

    (b) (i)   Calculate the energy in joules and in electronvolts of a photon of wavelength 590 nm.   [3 marks]

       (ii) Calculate the speed of an electron which will have the same wavelength as the photon in (b)(i).   [2 marks]

Q2   Electrons travelling at a speed of 3.5×10^6 ms⁻¹ exhibit wave properties.

    (a) Calculate the wavelength of these electrons.   [2 marks]

    (b) Calculate the speed of protons which would have the same wavelength as these electrons.   [2 marks]

    (c) Both electrons and protons were accelerated from rest by the same potential difference.
        Explain why they will have different wavelengths.
        (Hint: if they're accelerated by the same p.d., they have the same K.E.)   [3 marks]

Q3   An electron is accelerated through a potential difference of 6.0 kV.

    (a) Calculate its kinetic energy in joules, assuming no energy is lost in the process.   [2 marks]

    (b) Using the data above, calculate the speed of the electron.   [2 marks]

    (c) Calculate the de Broglie wavelength of the electron.   [2 marks]

Don't hide your wave-particles under a bushel...

*Right — I think we'll all agree that quantum physics is a wee bit strange when you come to think about it. What it's saying is that electrons and photons aren't really waves, and they aren't really particles — they're **both**... at the **same time**. It's what quantum physicists like to call a 'juxtaposition of states'. Well they would, wouldn't they...*

SECTION SIX — QUANTUM PHENOMENA

The "Sum Over Paths" Theory

These pages are for OCR B Unit 2 only.

So... you've got to grips with phasors... now here's where the really weird stuff kicks in. Buckle your seatbelts...and prepare to be amazed as the magical world of quantum reveals why light travels in straight lines, and why probability is a bit more useful than guessing what coloured ball you're likely to pick out of a bag...

Photons *try* Every Possible Path

1) A rather clever bloke called Richard Feynman came up with a completely different idea of how photons (or any subatomic particles, **quanta**) get from a source to a detector.

2) Feynman reckoned that instead of just taking one route to the detector, a photon will take **all** of the **possible paths** to the detector in one go. You can keep track of this photon whizzing along every possible route using **phasors** (see p 80).

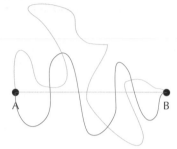

And all means <u>all</u> — the paths between A and B can be as squiggly as you like.

You *can use* Phasors *to Track Quanta*

1) Take **Young's double-slit experiment** (see p 86). You can use phasors to show how light or dark a certain spot on a screen will be. In quantum mechanics, you can use phasors to tell you how **probable** it is that a quantum (in this case a photon) will arrive there.

2) Take a photon travelling down **one particular path**.
   As it travels, its phasor will rotate (anticlockwise) until it reaches the detector. By knowing the energy of the photon, you can work out the **frequency** of the phasor's rotation, *f*, by rearranging Planck's formula.

$$f = \frac{E}{h}$$

Remember — E is the photon's energy and h is Planck's constant

3) You want to **record** the position of the phasor at the **end** of every path — you could then **sum** these phasors to find the **resultant phasor** for the photon making the journey from a source to a detector.

4) Of course you can't find the final phasor for every path as there's an **infinite** number of them. When you do the maths, nearly all the phasors cancel each other out — so you only need to consider the straightest/quickest possible paths (see p 100).

Example: Young's Double-Slit Experiment (again...)

1) Imagine that a photon is emitted by the source and hits point X on the screen. Take two of its possible paths and say it follows **both** of them, as shown.

2) The **phasor** of the photon along each path rotates at the **same rate** (because it's the **same photon** so the phasors will have the same frequency).

3) Because the photon has to travel slightly **further** on the green path, it takes slightly **longer** to reach point X. This means the final phasor for the green path will have **rotated** slightly **further** than that for the blue path.

4) You can find the **resultant** phasor arrow for the photon reaching point X by **adding** the final phasor position for each path, **tip-to-tail** (just like a normal vector sum (see p 4)).

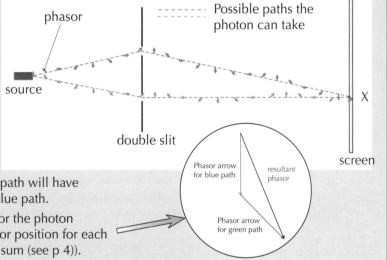

Quantum Behaviour *Applies to Any* Subatomic Particle

1) Remember it's **not just photons** that act like this — **all** subatomic particles do.

2) In **electron diffraction** it's exactly the same process. By summing the final phasor for every possible path, you can find how **likely** it is an electron will impact a fluorescent screen at a particular point.

3) The only difference is that when finding the **frequency** and **amplitude** of the electron phasor, *E* is the **kinetic energy** of the electron.

$$f = \frac{E_{kinetic}}{h}$$

The "Sum Over Paths" Theory

You can Calculate **Probability** from the **Resultant Phasor**

1) You can find the **probability** that a quantum will arrive at a point from **squaring** the **resultant phasor amplitude**.

$$\text{Probability} \propto (\text{Resultant phasor})^2$$

2) The **higher** the probability, the **more likely** the particle will arrive there (well der....).

3) If the **photon** is your quantum of choice, you can think of the **probability** and the **brightness** of the area as pretty much the same thing — the more **probable** it is that a photon will arrive at a point, the **brighter** it will appear.

Example

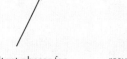

resultant phasor for photon hitting point X

magnitude = 2.5

resultant phasor for photon hitting point Y

magnitude = 1.34

The resultant phasor amplitudes are shown for the paths a photon could take to points X and Y. How many times brighter does point X appear than point Y? Explain your answer.

Square the magnitude of each phasor to find a number proportional to the probability of the photon arriving at each point.

Probability of photon hitting point X $\propto (2.5)^2 = $ **6.25**

Probability of photon hitting point Y $\propto (1.34)^2 = $ **1.80** (3 s.f.)

The more probable a photon will arrive at a point, the brighter it will be. So the relative probability of a photon arriving at the two points will be the relative brightness between the points.

So, point X appears $6.25 \div 1.80 = $ **3.5 times** brighter than point Y.

Practice Questions

Q1 What equation would you use to find the frequency of rotation of a photon phasor?

Q2 How are two phasor arrows combined to give a resultant?

Q3 How will a point appear if the probability for a light photon is zero there?

Exam Questions

Q1 The resultant phasors for an electron reaching points A and B have magnitudes of 6.3 and 4.5 respectively. How many times more likely is it that an electron will arrive at point A than point B? [4 marks]

Q2 A light photon has a frequency of 6.0×10^{14} Hz. How many times does the photon's phasor arrow rotate as it moves along a path 120 mm long from a source to a detector? ($c = 3.0 \times 10^8$ ms^{-1}.) [2 marks]

Q3 An electron has a velocity of 4.0×10^5 ms^{-1}. The mass of an electron is 9.1×10^{-31} kg and h = 6.6×10^{-34} Js.

(a) Calculate the kinetic energy of the electron. [1 mark]

(b) What is the frequency of rotation of its phasor? [2 marks]

Set your phasors to stun...

This all sounds a bit weird, but I guess it's only as bizarre sounding as saying light's a particle or a wave depending on its mood at the time. It also gives a brand new way of looking at your everyday physics fun like reflection...

Using "Sum Over Paths"

These pages are for OCR B Unit 2 only.

Feynman could have just been having a laugh, but the results from his theory hold up just as well as any other...

Reflections *in a* Plane Mirror *— Same Angle* Reflection is the Preferred Path

1) Imagine you're firing a photon at a mirror so that it **reflects** and hits a detector.

2) You normally just assume that when light bounces off a mirror, it takes the **quickest** possible path, where the **angle of incidence**, *i*, **equals** the **angle of reflection**, *r* (Path 3). But the sum over paths rule says a photon will take **every possible path**...

3) As before, you need to find the final position of the photon's phasor for **every possible path** (of course in practice you only look at a few), then add the final phasors to find the resultant.

4) What you find is that the paths **nearest** to the **quickest** path have phasors that almost **line up**, giving most of the amplitude of the resultant — and so **most** of the **probability** that the photon will reach the detector.

5) The final phasors for slower, longer paths near the ends of the mirror tend to '**curl up**' and almost cancel themselves out. They end up adding **almost nothing** to the resultant amplitude or the probability.

6) So quantum behaviour shows that **most** of the probability that a photon will arrive at the detector comes from the path you'd **classically expect** the light to take — the sum over paths rule **predicts** the rule of reflection.

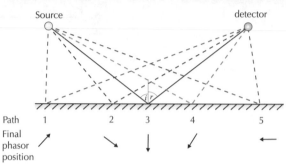

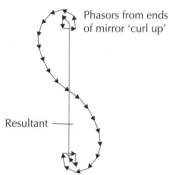

Phasors from ends of mirror 'curl up'

Resultant

The Path *that gives the* Highest Probability *is the* Quickest Route

1) The sum over paths rule predicts all sorts of physics laws we take for granted. And each time it seems to be down to the **same reason**:

> The final phasor of the **quickest path** will contribute the **most** to the **resultant amplitude** and the **probability** of a quantum arriving at a point.

2) It even predicts one of the most fundamental light behaviours — that **light** travels in a **straight line**. If you find the final phasors for every possible path, you get a similar pattern to the reflection experiment above. As a **straight line** is the shortest (and therefore **quickest**) path between two points — it provides the largest probability of a photon arriving at a particular point.

3) Obviously there are times when light **doesn't** travel in a straight line, like when it's being **refracted** — but quantum behaviour predicts that as well...

Example: Refraction

1) Imagine spotting a pineapple at the bottom of a swimming pool. What **route** does the light take from the pineapple to your eye? Altogether now... it takes **all of them**.

2) When light travels in water, it **slows down**, but its **frequency stays the same**. This means the photons still have the **same energy**, and a photon's phasor will still have the **same amplitude** and **frequency** of rotation **whatever** material it's travelling through.

3) If you add up all the phasors for all the possible paths, it's the path that takes the **shortest time** that contributes the most to the resultant amplitude and so to the probability that the photon will get to your eye.

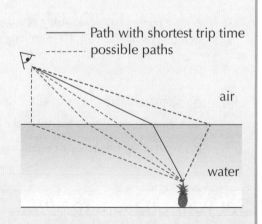

—— Path with shortest trip time
------ possible paths

air

water

Using "Sum Over Paths"

You Need *All Paths* to Take the *Same Time* to Focus *Quanta*

To **focus** photons (or any other quanta), you need to make sure all straight line paths (that follow the reflection or refraction rule) from the source to the focus point take the **same amount of time** — so the final phasors for every path will be in the same direction.

Example 1 — A Concave Mirror

The curve of a concave mirror has to be such that no matter which part of the mirror a photon hits, it will have taken the same time (and so travelled the same distance) when it reaches the focal point of the mirror.

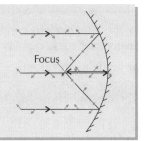

Example 2 — A Convex Lens

The paths towards the edges of the lens are **longer** than those that go through the middle. You make the time taken for each path the same by **increasing** the amount of **glass** in the **middle part** of the lens to increase the time it takes to travel along the shorter paths between the source and detector.

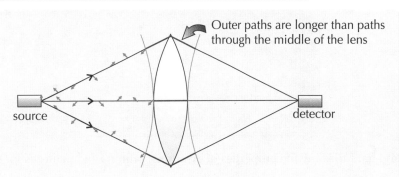

Outer paths are longer than paths through the middle of the lens

Practice Questions

Q1 Explain how the sum over paths theory predicts that light should travel in a straight line.

Q2 Describe how the sum over paths rule explains the path of reflected light.

Q3 Describe in terms of phasors how light is focused through a convex lens.

Exam Question

Q1 A photon travels from a source S through three slits onto a screen. The phasors for three paths the photon can take to each of two points on the screen, B and D, are shown below. (0.5 cm is equal to an amplitude of 3.)

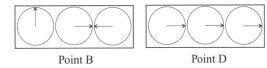

Point B   Point D

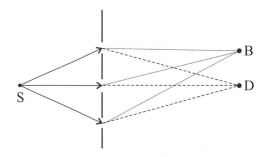

(a) Find the resultant phasor amplitude at
   i)   point B.   [1 mark]
   ii)   point D.   [1 mark]

(b) Explain why point B on the screen appears dimmer than point D.   [2 marks]

I ate all the pies — some would call it greed, I say it's photon thinking...

OK, so that's some pretty wacky sounding physics... but it does seem to work and agree with the standard physics laws we know and love... well, maybe not <u>love</u>. It's tricky, but you just need to follow the same method each time: sum the final phasors for all possible paths to get the resultant, then use the resultant to find the probability the quanta will get there.

Atomic Structure

These pages are for AQA A Unit 1 only (in fact, so is the rest of the section)

"So what did you do today Johnny?" "Particle Physics, Mum." "How nice dear — done with times tables then?"
*Yeah, well, it's not exactly the **easiest** topic in the world, but it's a darn sight more interesting than mechanics.*

*Atoms are made up of **Protons**, **Neutrons** and **Electrons***

Inside **every atom**, there's a **nucleus** containing **protons** and **neutrons**.
Protons and **neutrons** are both known as **nucleons**.   **Orbiting** this core are the **electrons**.

This is the **nuclear model** of the atom.

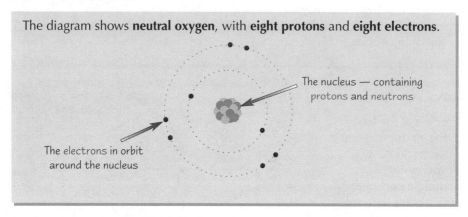

The diagram shows **neutral oxygen**, with **eight protons** and **eight electrons**.

The nucleus — containing protons and neutrons

The electrons in orbit around the nucleus

You have to know the **properties** of **electrons**, **protons** and **neutrons** for the exam — make sure you **learn this table**.

Particle	Charge	Relative Mass
Proton	Positive, +1	1
Neutron	Neutral, 0	1
Electron	Negative, –1	0.0005

*Atoms are **Really**, **Really Tiny***

Each atom is about a **tenth of a nanometre (1×10^{-10} m)** in **diameter**. To give you that in context,
you'd need to line up around **4 million iron atoms** side by side to give you a line **1 millimetre** long.

And if you think that's small, try the nucleus.

1)   Although the **proton** and **neutron** are **2000 times** more **massive** than the **electron**, the nucleus only takes up a **tiny proportion** of the atom. The electrons orbit at relatively **vast distances**.

2)   The nucleus is only one **10 000th the size** of the whole atom — most of the atom is **empty space**.

3)   If we were to **shrink** the **Solar System** (including poor rejected pluto) so the **Sun** was the **size of a gold nucleus**, **Pluto** would only be **half as far** away as **gold's furthest electron**.

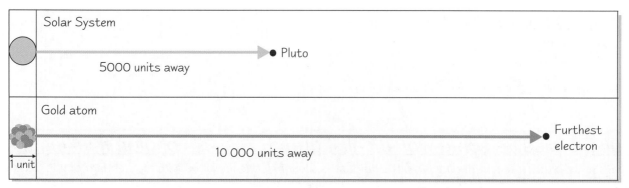

Solar System

5000 units away

• Pluto

Gold atom

1 unit

10 000 units away

Furthest electron

Mind-blowing isn't it. I try not to think too much about it...

Atomic Structure

The **Proton Number** is the **Number** of **Protons** in the Nucleus

No... really.

The **proton number** is sometimes called the **atomic number**, and has the **symbol Z** (I'm sure it makes sense to someone). **Z** is just the **number of protons** in the nucleus.

It's the **proton number** that **defines** the **element** — **no two elements** will have the **same** number of protons.

In a **neutral atom**, the number of **electrons equals** the number of **protons**.
The element's **reactions** and **chemical behaviour** depend on the number of **electrons**.
So the **proton number** tells you a lot about its **chemical properties**.

The **Nucleon Number** is the **Total Number** of **Protons** and **Neutrons**

The **nucleon number** is also called the **mass number**, and has the **symbol A** (*shrug*).
It tells you how many **protons** and **neutrons** are in the nucleus. Since each **proton or neutron** has an **atomic mass** of (approximately) **1** and the electrons weigh virtually nothing, the **number** of **nucleons** is the same as the **atom's mass**.

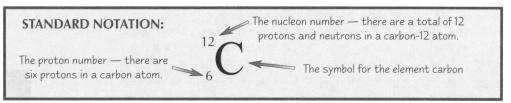

STANDARD NOTATION:

The nucleon number — there are a total of 12 protons and neutrons in a carbon-12 atom.

The proton number — there are six protons in a carbon atom.

$^{12}_{6}C$

The symbol for the element carbon

Isotopes have the **Same Proton Number**, but **Different Nucleon Numbers**

Atoms with the **same number of protons** but **different numbers of neutrons** are called **isotopes**.

Example: Hydrogen has three isotopes — hydrogen, deuterium and tritium

Hydrogen has 1 proton and 0 neutrons.
Deuterium has 1 proton and 1 neutron.
Tritium has 1 proton and 2 neutrons.

Changing the number of **neutrons doesn't affect** the atom's **chemical** properties.

The **number of neutrons** affects the **stability** of the nucleus though.

In **general**, the **greater** the number of **neutrons** compared with the number of **protons**, the **more unstable** the nucleus.

Unstable nuclei may be **radioactive** and **decay** to make themselves stable (see p105).

Practice Questions

Q1 List the particles that make up the atom and give their charges and relative masses.

Q2 Define the proton number and nucleon number.

Q3 What is an isotope?

Exam Questions

Q1 Describe the nuclear model of the atom. [3 marks]

Q2 How many protons, neutrons and electrons are there in a neutral atom of oxygen, $^{16}_{8}O$? [2 marks]

Q3 Define the term 'isotope'. Describe the similarities and differences between the properties of two isotopes of the same element. [3 marks]

"Proton no. = no. of protons" — not exactly nuclear physics is it... oh wait...

I dunno, I just can't get my head round that size of a nucleus stuff — it's just mind-blowing. I have enough trouble imagining this huge Solar System, never mind something so small that, by rights, shouldn't even exist. It's like trying to imagine infinity or something. Still... in true Physicist fashion, I don't let that bother me — I just learn the powers of 10 and everything's OK.

Stable and Unstable Nuclei

These pages are for AQA A Unit 1 only

Keeping the nucleus stable requires a lot of effort — a bit like AS Physics then...

The **Strong Nuclear Force** Binds Nucleons Together

There are several different **forces** acting on the nucleons in a nucleus. The two you already know about are **electromagnetic** forces from the protons' electric charges, and **gravitational** forces due to the masses of the particles.

If you do the calculations (don't worry, *you* don't have to) you find the repulsion from the **electrostatic force** is much, much **bigger** than the **gravitational** attraction. If these were the only forces acting in the nucleus, the nucleons would **fly apart**. So there must be **another attractive force** that **holds the nucleus together** — called the **strong nuclear force**. (The gravitational force is so small, you can just ignore it.)

The **strong nuclear force** is quite **complicated**:

1) To **hold the nucleus together**, the strong nuclear force must be an **attractive force** that's **stronger** than the electrostatic force. So far so good.

2) Experiments have shown that the strong nuclear force has a **very short range**. It can only hold nucleons together when they're separated by up to **a few femtometres** (1 fm = 1×10^{-15} m) — the size of a nucleus.

3) The **strength** of the strong nuclear force **quickly falls** beyond this distance (see the graph below).

4) Experiments also show that the strong nuclear force **works equally between all nucleons**. This means that the size of the force is the same whether it's proton-proton, neutron-neutron or proton-neutron.

5) At **very small separations**, the strong nuclear force must be **repulsive** — otherwise there would be nothing to stop it **crushing** the nucleus to a **point**.

lime green, orange and day-glow pink — repulsive at small separations

The **Size** of the Strong Nuclear Force **Varies** with **Nucleon Separation**

The **strong nuclear force** can be plotted on a **graph** to show how it changes with the **distance of separation** between **nucleons**. If the **electrostatic force** is also plotted, you can see the **relationship** between these **two forces**.

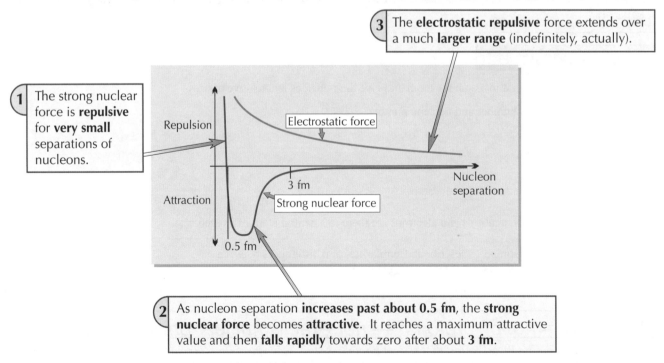

3 The **electrostatic repulsive** force extends over a much **larger range** (indefinitely, actually).

1 The strong nuclear force is **repulsive** for **very small** separations of nucleons.

2 As nucleon separation **increases past about 0.5 fm**, the **strong nuclear force** becomes **attractive**. It reaches a maximum attractive value and then **falls rapidly** towards zero after about **3 fm**.

Stable and Unstable Nuclei

α Emission Happens in Very Big Nuclei

1) **Alpha emission** only happens in **very big** atoms (with more than 82 protons), like **uranium** and **radium**.

2) The **nuclei** of these atoms are just **too big** for the strong nuclear force to keep them stable.

3) When an alpha particle is **emitted**:

> The **proton number decreases** by **two**, and the **nucleon number decreases** by **four**.

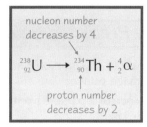

nucleon number decreases by 4

$$^{238}_{92}U \longrightarrow {}^{234}_{90}Th + {}^{4}_{2}\alpha$$

proton number decreases by 2

β⁻ Emission Happens in Neutron-Rich Nuclei

1) **Beta-minus** (usually just called beta) decay is the emission of an **electron** from the **nucleus** along with an **antineutrino**.

2) Beta decay happens in isotopes that are **"neutron rich"** (i.e. have too many more **neutrons** than **protons** in their nucleus).

3) When a nucleus ejects a beta particle, one of the **neutrons** in the nucleus is **changed** into a **proton**.

> The **proton number increases** by **one**, and the **nucleon number stays the same**.

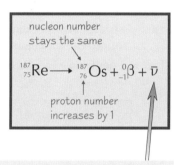

nucleon number stays the same

$$^{187}_{75}Re \longrightarrow {}^{187}_{76}Os + {}^{0}_{-1}\beta + \bar{\nu}$$

proton number increases by 1

> In beta decay, you get a **tiny neutral particle** called an **antineutrino** released. This antineutrino carries away some **energy** and **momentum**. There's more about neutrinos and antineutrinos on the next few pages.

Practice Questions

Q1 What causes an electrostatic force inside the nucleus?

Q2 What evidence suggests the existence of a strong nuclear force?

Q3 Is the strong interaction attractive or repulsive at a nucleon separation of 10 fm?

Q4 Describe the changes that happen in the nucleus during alpha and beta-minus decay.

Exam Questions

Q1 The strong nuclear force binds the nucleus together.

(a) Explain why the force must be repulsive at very short distances. [1 mark]

(b) How does the strong interaction limit the size of a stable nucleus? [2 marks]

Q2 Radium-226 and potassium-40 are both unstable isotopes.

(a) Radium-226 undergoes alpha decay to radon. Complete the balanced nuclear equation for this reaction: [3 marks]

$$^{226}_{88}Ra \longrightarrow {}^{222}_{86}Rn + {}^{4}_{2}\alpha$$

(b) Potassium-40 (Z = 19, A = 40) undergoes beta decay to calcium. Write a balanced nuclear equation for this reaction. [4 marks]

$$^{40}_{19}K \longrightarrow {}^{40}_{20}Ca + {}^{0}_{-1}\beta + \bar{\nu}_e$$

The strong interaction's like nuclear glue...

*In every nuclear reaction energy, momentum, charge, and nucleon number (and several other things that you'll find out about over the next few pages) are conserved. That's why the antineutrino in beta decay **has** to be there.*

Particles and Antiparticles

These pages are for AQA A Unit 1 only

"I cannae do it Cap'n — their electron-antineutrino ray gun's interfering with my antineutron positron reading..."

Antiparticles were Predicted Before they were Discovered

When **Paul Dirac** wrote down an equation obeyed by **electrons**, he found a kind of **mirror image** solution.

1) It predicted the existence of a particle like the **electron** but with **opposite electric charge**.

2) The **positron** turned up later in a cosmic ray experiment. Positrons have **identical mass** (and identical energy in MeV — see p90) to electrons but they carry a **positive** charge.

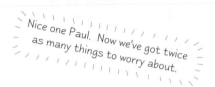

Nice one Paul. Now we've got twice as many things to worry about.

Every Particle has an Antiparticle

Each particle type has a **corresponding antiparticle** with the **same mass** but with **opposite charge** (and in other ways too). For instance, an **antiproton** is a **negatively-charged** particle with the same mass as the **proton**.

Even the shadowy **neutrino** (see p109) has an antiparticle version called the **antineutrino** — it doesn't do much either.

Particle	Symbol	Charge	Antiparticle	Symbol	Charge
proton	p	+1	antiproton	$\bar{p}$	−1
neutron	n	0	antineutron	$\bar{n}$	0
electron	e	−1	positron	e^+	+1
electron-neutrino	ν_e	0	electron-antineutrino	$\bar{\nu}_e$	0

You can Create Matter and Antimatter from Energy

You've probably heard about the **equivalence** of energy and mass. It all comes out of Einstein's Special Theory of Relativity. **Energy** can turn into **mass** and **mass** can turn into **energy** if you know how. You can work it all out using the formula $E = mc^2$ but you won't be expected to do the calculations for AS.

It's a good thing this doesn't randomly happen all the time or else you could end up with cute bunny rabbits popping up and exploding unexpectedly all over the place. Oh, the horror...

As you've probably guessed, there's a bit **more to it** than that:

> When **energy** is converted into **mass** you get **equal amounts** of **matter** and **antimatter**.

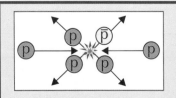

Fire **two protons** at each other at high speed and you'll end up with a lot of **energy** at the point of impact. This energy might be converted into **more particles**.

If an extra **proton** is formed then there will always be an **antiproton** to go with it. It's called **pair production**.

Particles and Antiparticles

Each *Particle-Antiparticle Pair* is Produced from a *Single Photon*

Pair production only happens if **one gamma ray photon** has enough energy to produce that much mass. It also tends to happen near a **nucleus**, which helps conserve momentum.

You usually get **electron-positron** pairs produced (rather than any other pair) — because they have a relatively **low mass**.

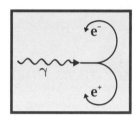

The particle tracks are curved because there's usually a magnetic field present in particle physics experiments. They curve in opposite directions because of the opposite charges on the electron and positron.

The *Opposite* of *Pair-Production* is *Annihilation*

When a **particle** meets its **antiparticle** the result is **annihilation**. All the **mass** of the particle and antiparticle gets converted back to **energy**. Antiparticles can only exist for a fraction of a second before this happens, so you don't get them in ordinary matter.

The electron and positron annihilate and their mass is converted into the energy of a pair of gamma ray photons.

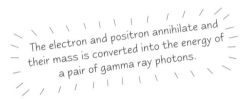

OR

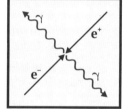

Mesons are Their *Own Antiparticles*

(Don't worry if you don't know what a meson — look at the next page. This just seemed like a good place to put it.)

Just before you leave this bit it's worth mentioning that the π^- meson (a type of exotic particle) is just the **antiparticle** of the π^+ meson (another exotic particle), and the **antiparticle** of a π^0 meson is **itself**. You'll see why on p110.
So we don't need any more particles here... Phew.

Practice Questions

Q1   Describe the properties of an electron-antineutrino.

Q2   What is pair production?

Q3   What happens when a proton collides with an antiproton?

Exam Questions

Q1   Write down an equation for the reaction between a positron and an electron and give the name for this type of reaction.   [2 marks]

Q2   According to Einstein, mass and energy are equivalent.
Explain why the mass of a block of iron cannot be converted directly into energy.   [2 marks]

Q3   Give a reason why the reaction: $\mathbf{p} + \mathbf{p} \rightarrow \mathbf{p} + \mathbf{p} + \mathbf{n}$ is not possible.   [1 mark]

This really is Physics at its ~~hardest~~ grooviest...

Inertial dampers are off-line Captain.........oops, no — it's just these false ears making me feel dizzy.
Anyway — you'd need to carry an awful lot of antimatter to provide enough energy to run a spaceship.
It's not easy to store, either. So it'd never work in real life.

Classification of Particles

These pages are for AQA A Unit 1 only

There are loads of different types of particle, apart from the ones you get in normal matter (protons, neutrons, etc.). They only appear in cosmic rays and in particle accelerators, and they often decay very quickly so they're difficult to get a handle on. Nonetheless, you need to learn about a load of them and their properties.

Stick with it — you'll get there.

Hadrons *are* Particles *that Feel the* Strong Nuclear Force *(e.g. Protons and Neutrons)*

1) The **nucleus** of an atom is made up from **protons** and **neutrons** (déjà vu).

2) Since the **protons** are **positively charged** they need a strong force to hold them together — the **strong nuclear force** or the **strong interaction** (who said physicists lack imagination...). See page 104 for details.

(Leptons are an example of particles that can't. See next page.)

3) **Not all particles** can **feel** the **strong nuclear force** — the ones that **can** are called **hadrons**.

4) Hadrons aren't **fundamental** particles. They're made up of **smaller particles** called **quarks** (see pages 110-111).

5) There are **two** types of **hadron** — **baryons** and **mesons**.

Protons *and* Neutrons *are* Baryons

1) It's helpful to think of **protons** and **neutrons** as **two versions** of the **same particle** — the **nucleon**. They just have **different electric charges**.

2) As well as **protons** and **neutrons**, there are **other baryons** that you don't get in normal matter — like **sigmas** (Σ) — they're **short-lived** and you **don't** need to **know about them** for AS (woohoo!).

The Proton *is the* Only Stable Baryon

All baryons except protons decay to a **proton**.
Most physicists think that protons don't **decay**.

Some theories predict that protons should decay with a very long half-life but there's no evidence for it at the moment.

Baryon and Meson felt the strong interaction.

The Number of Baryons *in an interaction is called the* Baryon Number

Baryon number is the number of baryons. (A bit like **nucleon number** but including unusual baryons like Σ too.)
The **proton** and the **neutron** each have a baryon number **B = +1**.
The **total baryon number** in **any** particle interaction **never changes**.

The Mesons *You Need to Know About are* Pions *and* Kaons

1) **All mesons** are **unstable** and have **baryon number B = 0** (because they're not baryons).

2) **Pions** (π-mesons) are the **lightest mesons**. You get **three versions** with different **electric charges** — π^+, π^0 and π^-. Pions were **discovered** in **cosmic rays**. You get **loads** of them in **high-energy particle collisions** like those studied at the **CERN** particle accelerator.

3) **Kaons** (K-mesons) are **heavier** and more **unstable** than **pions**. You get different ones like K^+ and K^0.

4) Mesons **interact** with **baryons** via the **strong force**.

Pion interactions swap p's with n's and n's with p's, but leave the overall baryon number unchanged.

Summary *of* Hadron Properties

DON'T PANIC if you don't understand all this yet. For now, just **learn** these properties. You'll need to work through to the end of page 111 to see how it **all fits together**.

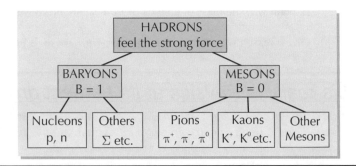

Classification of Particles

Leptons Don't feel the Strong Interaction (e.g. Electrons and Neutrinos)

1) **Leptons** are **fundamental particles** and they **don't** feel the **strong nuclear force**. They only really **interact** with other particles is via the **weak interaction** (along with a bit due to the gravitational force and the electromagnetic force as well if they're charged).

2) **Electrons** (e^-) are **stable** and very **familiar** but — you guessed it — there are also **two more leptons** called the **muon** (μ^-) and the **tau** (τ^-) that are just like **heavy electrons**.

3) **Muons** and **taus** are **unstable**, and **decay** eventually into **ordinary electrons**.

4) The **electron**, **muon** and **tau** leptons each come with their **own neutrino**, ν_e, ν_μ and ν_τ.

5) **Neutrinos** have **zero** or **almost zero mass** and **zero electric charge** — so they don't do much. **Neutrinos** only take part in **weak interactions** (see p111). In fact, a neutrino can **pass right through the Earth** without **anything** happening to it.

You Have to Count the Three Types of Lepton Separately

Each lepton is given a **lepton number** of **+1**, but the **electron**, **muon** and **tau** types of lepton have to be **counted separately**.

You get **three different** lepton numbers L_e, L_μ and L_τ.

Name	Symbol	Charge	L_e	L_μ	L_τ
electron	e^-	-1	$+1$	0	0
electron-neutrino	ν_e	0	$+1$	0	0
muon	μ^-	-1	0	$+1$	0
muon-neutrino	ν_μ	0	0	$+1$	0
tau	τ^-	-1	0	0	$+1$
tau-neutrino	ν_τ	0	0	0	$+1$

Like the baryon number, the lepton number is just the number of leptons.

Neutrons Decay into Protons

The **neutron** is an **unstable particle** that **decays** into a **proton**.
It's really just an **example** of β^- decay which is caused by the **weak interaction** (see p111).

$$n \rightarrow p + e^- + \bar{\nu}_e$$

The antineutrino has $L_e = -1$ so the total lepton number is zero.

Practice Questions

Q1 List the differences between a hadron and a lepton.

Q2 Which is the only stable baryon (probably)?

Q3 A particle collision at CERN produces 2 protons, 3 pions and 1 neutron. What is the total baryon number of these particles?

Q4 Which two particles have lepton number $L_\tau = +1$?

Exam Questions

Q1 List all the decay products of the neutron. Explain why this decay cannot be due to the strong interaction. [3 marks]

Q2 Initially, the muon was incorrectly identified as a meson. Explain why the muon is not a meson. [3 marks]

Go back to the top of page 108 — do not pass GO, do not collect £200...

Do it. Go back and read it again. I promise — read these pages about 3 or 4 times and you'll start to see a pattern. There are hadrons that feel the force, leptons that don't. Hadrons are either baryons or mesons, and they're all weird except for those well-known baryons: protons and neutrons. There are loads of leptons, including good old electrons.

Quarks

These pages are for AQA A Unit 1 only

*If you haven't read pages 106 to 109, do it now! For the rest of you — here are the **juicy bits** you've been waiting for.*
*Particle physics makes **a lot more sense** when you look at quarks. More sense than it did before anyway.*

Quarks *are* Fundamental Particles

Quarks are the **building blocks** for **hadrons** (baryons and mesons).

If that first sentence doesn't make much sense to you, <u>read pages 106-109</u> — you have been warned... twice.

1) To make **protons** and **neutrons** you only need two types of quark — the **up** quark (**u**) and the **down** quark (**d**).
2) An extra one called the **strange** quark (**s**) lets you make more particles with a property called **strangeness**.

Antiparticles of hadrons are made from **antiquarks**.

Particle physicists have found six different quarks altogether but you only need to know about three of them.

Quarks *and* Antiquarks *have* Opposite Properties

The **antiquarks** have **opposite properties** to the quarks — as you'd expect.

QUARKS

name	symbol	charge	baryon number	strangeness
up	u	$+\,^{2}/_{3}$	$+\,^{1}/_{3}$	0
down	d	$-\,^{1}/_{3}$	$+\,^{1}/_{3}$	0
strange	s	$-\,^{1}/_{3}$	$+\,^{1}/_{3}$	-1

ANTIQUARKS

name	symbol	charge	baryon number	strangeness
anti-up	$\bar{u}$	$-\,^{2}/_{3}$	$-\,^{1}/_{3}$	0
anti-down	$\bar{d}$	$+\,^{1}/_{3}$	$-\,^{1}/_{3}$	0
anti-strange	$\bar{s}$	$+\,^{1}/_{3}$	$-\,^{1}/_{3}$	$+1$

Baryons *are Made from* Three Quarks

Evidence for quarks came from **hitting protons** with **high-energy electrons**.
The way the **electrons scattered** showed that there were **three concentrations of charge** (quarks) **inside** the proton.

Proton = **uud**

Total charge
= 2/3 + 2/3 − 1/3 = 1

Baryon number
= 1/3 + 1/3 + 1/3 = 1

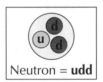

Neutron = **udd**

Total charge
= 2/3 − 1/3 − 1/3 = 0

Baryon number
= 1/3 + 1/3 + 1/3 = 1

Antiprotons are $\overline{\textbf{uud}}$ and antineutrons are $\overline{\textbf{udd}}$ — so no surprises there then.

Mesons *are a* Quark *and an* Antiquark

Pions are just made from combinations of **up**, **down**, **anti-up** and **anti-down** quarks. **Kaons** have strangeness so you need to put in **s** quarks as well (remember that the **s** quark has a strangeness of S = −1).

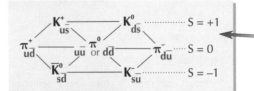

Physicists love patterns. Gaps in patterns like this predicted the existence of particles that were actually found later in experiments. Great stuff.

There's *No Such Thing* as a *Free Quark*

What if you **blasted** a **proton** with **enough energy** — could you **separate out** the quarks? Nope.
Your energy just gets changed into more **quarks and antiquarks** — it's **pair production** again and you just make **mesons**. It's not possible to get a quark by itself — this is called **quark confinement**.

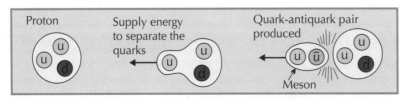

Quarks

The **Weak Interaction** is something that Changes the **Quark Type**

In β⁻ decay a **neutron** is changed into a **proton** — in other words **udd** changes into **uud**.
It means turning a **d** quark into a **u** quark. Only the weak interaction can do this.

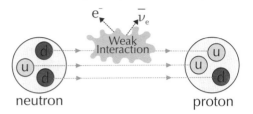

neutron   proton

Some unstable isotopes like **carbon-11** decay by β⁺ emission. In this case a **proton** changes to a **neutron**, so a **u** quark changes to a **d** quark and we get:

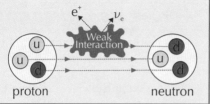

proton   neutron

Four Properties are **Conserved** in **Particle Reactions**

Charge and **Baryon Number** are **Always** Conserved

In **any** particle reaction, the **total charge** after the reaction must equal the total charge before the reaction. The same goes for **baryon number**.

Strangeness is Conserved in **Strong Interactions**

The **only** way to change the **type** of quark is with the **weak interaction**, so in strong interactions there has to be the same number of strange quarks at the beginning as at the end. The reaction $K^- + p \rightarrow n + \pi^0$ is fine for **charge** and **baryon number** but not for **strangeness** — so it won't happen. The negative kaon has an **s** quark in it.

Conservation of **Lepton Number** is a Bit More **Complicated**

The **three types** of lepton number have to be conserved **separately**.

1)   For example, the reaction
      $\pi^- \rightarrow \mu^- + \bar{\nu}_\mu$ has $L_\mu = 0$ at the start and $L_\mu = 1 - 1 = 0$ at the end, so it's OK.
2)   On the other hand, the reaction $\nu_\mu + \mu^- \rightarrow e^- + \nu_e$ can't happen.
      At the start $L_\mu = 2$ and $L_e = 0$ but at the end $L_\mu = 0$ and $L_e = 2$.

Practice Questions

Q1   What is a quark?

Q2   Which type of particle is made from a quark and an antiquark?

Q3   Describe how a neutron is made up from quarks.

Q4   List four quantities that are conserved in particle interactions.

Exam Questions

Q1   Give the quark composition of the π⁻ and explain how the charges of the quarks give rise to its charge.   [2 marks]

Q2   Explain how the quark composition is changed in the β⁻ decay of the neutron.   [2 marks]

Q3   Give two reasons why the reaction $p + p \rightarrow p + K^+$ does not happen.   [2 marks]

A physical property called strangeness — how cool is that...

*True, there's a lot of information here, but this page really does **tie up** a lot of the stuff on the last few pages. Learn as much as you can from this double-page spread, then **go back** to page 106, and **work back** through to here. **Don't expect** to understand it all — but you will **definitely** find it **much easier to learn** when you can see how all the bits **fit in together**.*

Exchange Particles and Feynman Diagrams

These pages are for AQA A Unit 1 only

*Having learnt about hadrons (baryons and mesons) and leptons, antiparticles and quarks, you now have the esteemed privilege of learning about yet another weirdy thing called a **gauge boson**. To the casual observer this might not seem **entirely fair**. And I have to say, I'd be with them.*

Forces are Caused by Particle Exchange

You can't have **instantaneous action at a distance** (according to Einstein, anyway). So, when two particles **interact**, something must **happen** to let one particle know that the other one's there. That's the idea behind **exchange particles**.

1) **Repulsion** — Each time the **ball** is **thrown or caught** the people get **pushed apart**. It happens because the ball carries **momentum**.

   Particle exchange also explains **attraction**, but you need a bit more imagination.

2) **Attraction** — Each time the **boomerang** is **thrown or caught** the people **get pushed together**. (In real life, you'd probably fall in first.)

These exchange particles are called **gauge bosons**.

The **repulsion** between two **protons** is caused by the **exchange** of **virtual photons**, which are the gauge bosons of the **electromagnetic** force. Gauge bosons are **virtual** particles — they only exist for a **very short time**.

There are Four Fundamental Forces

All forces in nature are caused by four **fundamental** forces.
Each one has its **own gauge boson** and you have to learn their names:

Type of Interaction	Gauge Boson	Particles Affected
strong	gluon	hadrons only
electromagnetic	photon (symbol, γ)	charged particles only
weak	W^+, W^-, Z^0	all types
gravity	graviton?	all types

Particle physicists never bother about gravity because it's so incredibly feeble compared with the other types of interaction. Gravity only really matters when you've got big masses like stars and planets.

The graviton may exist but there's no evidence for it.

The Larger the Mass of the Gauge Boson, the Shorter the Range of the Force

1) The **W bosons** have a **mass** of about **100 times that of a proton**, which gives the weak force a **very short range**. Creating a **virtual W particle** uses **so much energy** that it can only exist for a **very short time** and it **can't travel far**.

2) On the other hand, the **photon** has **zero mass**, which gives you a force with **infinite range**.

Feynman Diagrams Show What's Going In and What's Coming Out

Richard Feynman was a brilliant physicist who was famous for explaining complicated ideas in a fun way that actually made sense. He worked out a really **neat way** of **solving problems** by **drawing pictures** rather than doing **calculations**.

1) **Gauge bosons** are represented by **wiggly lines** (technical term).

2) Other **particles** are represented by **straight lines**.

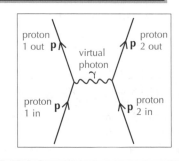

Exchange Particles and Feynman Diagrams

You can draw Feynman diagrams for **loads** of interactions but you **only** need to learn the ones on **this page** for your exam.

Beta-plus and Beta-minus Decay

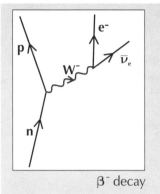 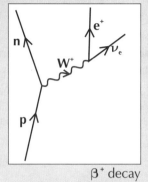

β⁻ decay β⁺ decay

$$n \rightarrow p + e^- + \bar{\nu}_e$$

$$p \rightarrow n + e^+ + \nu_e$$

You get an **antineutrino** in β⁻ decay and a **neutrino** in β⁺ decay so that **lepton number** is conserved.

RULES FOR DRAWING FEYNMAN DIAGRAMS:
1) **Incoming** particles start at the bottom of the diagram and move upwards.
2) The **baryons** stay on one side of the diagram, and the **leptons** stay on the other side.
3) The **W** bosons carry **charge** from one side of the diagram to the other — make sure charges balance.
4) A **W⁻** particle going to the **left** has the same effect as a **W⁺** particle going to the **right**.

A Proton Capturing an Electron

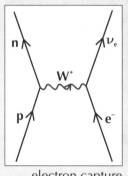

electron capture

Electrons and protons are of course attracted by the **electromagnetic interaction** between them, but if they **collide** the **weak interaction** can make this interaction happen.

$$p + e^- \rightarrow n + \nu_e$$

Neutrinos Interacting with Matter

There's a very **low probability** of a **neutrino interacting with matter**, but here's what happens when they do.

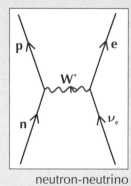 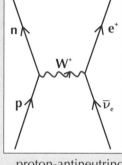

neutron-neutrino collision proton-antineutrino collision

$$n + \nu_e \rightarrow p + e^-$$

$$p + \bar{\nu}_e \rightarrow n + e^+$$

Practice Questions

Q1 List the four fundamental forces in nature.

Q2 Explain what a virtual particle is.

Q3 Draw the Feynman diagram for a neutrino-neutron interaction.

Q4 Which gauge bosons are exchanged in weak interactions?

Exam Questions

Q1 How is the force of electromagnetic repulsion between two protons explained by particle exchange? [2 marks]

Q2 Draw a Feynman diagram for the collision between an electron-antineutrino and a proton. Label the particles and state clearly which type of interaction is involved. [3 marks]

I need a drink...

Urrrgghhhh... eyes... glazed... brain... melting... ears... bleeding... help me... help me...

help me...

Error Analysis

Science is all about getting good evidence to test your theories... and part of that is knowing how good the results from an experiment are. Physicists always have to include the uncertainty in a result, so you can see the range the actual value probably lies within. Dealing with error and uncertainty is an important skill, so those pesky examiners like to sneak in a couple of questions about it... but if you know your stuff you can get some easy marks.

Nothing is Certain

1) **Every** measurement you take has an **experimental uncertainty**. Say you've done something outrageous like measure the length of a piece of wire with a centimetre ruler. You might think you've measured its length as 30 cm, but at **best** you've probably measured it to be 30 **± 0.5** cm. And that's without taking into account any other errors that might be in your measurement...

2) The **±** bit gives you the **range** in which the **true** length (the one you'd really like to know) probably lies — 30 ± 0.5 cm tells you the true length is very likely to lie in the range of 29.5 to 30.5 cm.

3) The smaller the uncertainty, the nearer your value must be to the true value, so the more **accurate** your result.

4) There are **two types** of **error** that cause experimental uncertainty:

Random errors

1) No matter how hard you try, you **can't get rid** of random errors.

2) They can just be down to **noise** (p.72), or that you're measuring a **random process** such as nuclear radiation emission.

3) You get random error in **any** measurement. If you measured the length of a wire 20 times, the chances are you'd get a **slightly different** value each time, e.g. due to your head being in a slightly different position when reading the scale.

4) It could be that you just can't keep controlled variables **exactly** the same throughout the experiment.

5) Or it could just be the wind was blowing in the wrong direction at the time...

Systematic errors

1) You get systematic errors not because you've made a mistake in a measurement — but because of the **apparatus** you're using, or your experimental method. E.g. using an inaccurate clock.

2) The problem is often that you **don't know they're there**. You've got to spot them first to have any chance of correcting for them.

3) Systematic errors usually **shift** all of your results to be too high or too low by the **same amount**. They're annoying, but there are things you can do to reduce them if you manage to spot them...

Lorraine thought getting an uncertainty of ± 0.1 A deserved a victory dance.

You Need to Know How to Improve Measurements

There are a few different ways you can **reduce** the uncertainty in your results:

Repeating measurements — by repeating a measurement **several times** and **averaging**, you reduce the **random uncertainty** in your result. The **more** measurements you average over, the **less error** you're likely to have.

Use higher precision apparatus — the **more precisely** you can measure something, the **less random error** there is in the measurement. So if you use more precise equipment — e.g. swapping a millimetre ruler for a micrometer to measure the diameter of a wire — you can instantly cut down the **random error** in your experiment.

Calibration — you can calibrate your apparatus by measuring a **known value**. If there's a **difference** between the **measured** and **known** value, you can use this to **correct** the inaccuracy of the apparatus, and so reduce your **systematic error**.

You can Calculate the Percentage Uncertainty in a Measurement

1) You might get asked to work out the percentage uncertainty in a measurement.

2) It's just working out a percentage, so nothing too tricky. It's just that sometimes you can get **the fear** as soon as you see the word uncertainty... but just keep your cool and you can pick up some easy marks.

Example

Tom finds the resistance of a filament lamp to be **5.0 ± 0.4** Ω.

The percentage uncertainty in the resistance measured $= \dfrac{0.4}{5.0} \times 100 = \mathbf{8\%}$

Error Analysis

You can Estimate Values by Averaging

You might be given a graph of information showing the results for many **repetitions** of the **same** experiment, and asked to estimate the true value and give an uncertainty in that value. Yuk. Here's how to go about it:

1) Estimate the true value by **averaging** the results you've been given.
   (Make sure you state whatever average it is you take, otherwise you might not get the mark.)

2) To get the uncertainty, you just need to look how far away from your average value the maximum and minimum values in the graph you've been given are.

Example — Estimating the resistance of a component

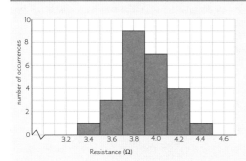

A class measure the resistance of a component and record their results on the bar chart shown. Estimate the resistance of the component, giving a suitable range of uncertainty in your answer.

There were 25 measurements, so taking the **mean**:

$$\frac{(3.4 + (3.6 \times 3) + (3.8 \times 9) + (4.0 \times 7) + (4.2 \times 4) + 4.4)}{25} = \frac{97.6}{25} = 3.90 \text{ (3 s.f.)}$$

The maximum value found was 4.4 Ω, the minimum value was 3.4. Both values are both about 0.5 Ω from the average value, so the answer is **3.9 ± 0.5 Ω**.

Error Bars to Show Uncertainty on a Graph

1) Most of the time in science, you work out the uncertainty in your **final result** using the uncertainty in **each measurement** you make.

2) When you're plotting a graph, you show the uncertainty in a value by using **error bars** to show the range the point is likely to lie in.

3) You probably won't get asked to **plot** any error bars (phew...) — but you might need to **read off** a graph that has them.

> Be careful — sometimes error bars are calculated using a set percentage of uncertainty for each measurement so will change depending on the measurement.

Example

Use the graph below to find the error in measuring the extension of material X.

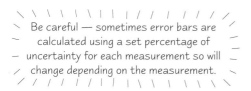

2 squares = 2 mm

The error bars extend 2 squares above and below each measurement, which is equivalent to 2 mm.

So, the uncertainty in each measurement is **± 2 mm**.

You can Estimate the Uncertainty of the Graph's Gradient

1) Normally when you draw a graph you'll want to find the gradient or intercept. E.g. for a force-extension graph, the gradient's 1/**k**, the stiffness constant of the material.

2) To find the value of **k**, you draw a nice line of best fit on the graph and calculate your answer from that. No problem there.

3) You can then draw the **maximum** and **minimum** slopes possible for the data through **all** of the error bars. By calculating the value of the gradient (or intercept) for these slopes, you can find maximum and minimum values the true answer is likely to lie between. And that's the **uncertainty** in your answer.

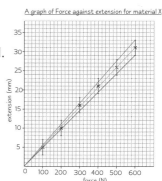

Random error in your favour — collect £200...

These pages should give you a fair idea of how to deal with errors... which are rather annoyingly in everything. Even if you're lucky enough to not get tested on this sort of thing in the exam, it's really useful to know for your lab coursework.

Answers

Section One — Mechanics

Page 5 — Scalars and Vectors

1) Start by drawing a diagram:

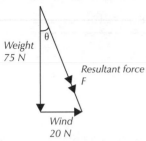

Weight
75 N

θ

Resultant force
F

Wind
20 N

$F^2 = 20^2 + 75^2 = 6025$
So $F = 77.6$ N
$\tan\theta = 20 / 75 = 0.267$
So $\theta = 14.9°$
The resultant force on the rock is 77.6 N [1 mark]
at an angle of 14.9° [1 mark] to the vertical.
Make sure you know which angle you're finding — and label it on your diagram.

2) Again, start by drawing a diagram:

horizontal component, v_H

15°

vertical component, v_v

velocity
20.0 ms⁻¹

horizontal component $v_H = 20\cos15° = 19.3$ ms⁻¹ [1 mark]
vertical component $v_v = 20\sin15° = 5.2$ ms⁻¹ downwards [1 mark]
Always draw a diagram.

Page 7 — Motion with Constant Acceleration

1)a) $a = -9.81$ ms⁻², $t = 5$ s, $u = 0$ ms⁻¹, $v = ?$
use : $\quad v = u + at$
$\qquad v = 0 + 5 \times -9.81$ [1 mark for either step of working]
$\qquad v = -49.05$ ms⁻¹ [1 mark]
NB: It's negative because she's falling downwards and we took upwards as the positive direction.

b) Use: $s = \left(\dfrac{u+v}{2}\right)t$ or $\quad s = ut + \frac{1}{2}at^2$ [1 mark for either]

$s = \dfrac{-49.05}{2} \times 5$ $\qquad s = 0 + \frac{1}{2} \times -9.81 \times 5^2$

$s = -122.625$ m $\qquad s = -122.625$ m
So she fell 122.625 m [1 mark for answer]

2)a) $v = 0$ ms⁻¹, $t = 3.2$ s, $s = 40$ m, $u = ?$

use: $s = \left(\dfrac{u+v}{2}\right)t$ [1 mark]

$40 = 3.2u \div 2$

$u = \dfrac{80}{3.2} = 25$ ms⁻¹ [1 mark]

b) use: $v^2 = u^2 + 2as$ [1 mark]
$\quad 0 = 25^2 + 80a$
$-80a = 625$
$\quad a = -7.8$ ms⁻² [1 mark]

3)a) Take upstream as negative: $v = 5$ ms⁻¹, $a = 6$ ms⁻², $s = 1.2$ m, $u = ?$
use: $v^2 = u^2 + 2as$ [1 mark]
$5^2 = u^2 + 2 \times 6 \times 1.2$
$u^2 = 25 - 14.4 = 10.6$
$u = -3.26$ ms⁻¹ [1 mark]

b) From furthest point: $u = 0$ ms⁻¹, $a = 6$ ms⁻², $v = 5$ ms⁻¹, $s = ?$
use: $v^2 = u^2 + 2as$ [1 mark]
$5^2 = 0 + 2 \times 6 \times s$
$s = 25 \div 12 = 2.08$ m [1 mark]

Page 9 — Free Fall

1)a) The computer needs:
The time for the first strip of card to pass through the beam [1 mark]
The time for the second strip of card to pass through the beam [1 mark]
The time between these events [1 mark]

b) Average speed of first strip while it breaks the light beam =
$\qquad$ width of strip ÷ time to pass through beam [1 mark]
Average speed of second strip while it breaks the light beam =
$\qquad$ width of strip ÷ time to pass through beam [1 mark]
Acceleration = (second speed – first speed)
$\qquad$ ÷ time between light beam being broken [1 mark]

c) E.g. the device will accelerate while the beam is broken by the strips. [1 mark]

2)a) You know $s = 5$ m, $a = -g$, $v = 0$
You need to find u, so use $v^2 = u^2 + 2as$
$0 = u^2 - 2 \times 9.81 \times 5$ [1 mark for either line of working]
$u^2 = 98.1$, so $u = 9.9$ ms⁻¹ [1 mark]

b) You know $a = -g$, $v = 0$ at highest pt, $u = 9.9$ ms⁻¹ from a)
You need to find t, so use $v = u + at$
$0 = 9.9 - 9.81t$ [1 mark for either line of working]
$t = 9.9/9.81 = 1.0$ s [1 mark]

c) Her velocity as she lands back on the trampoline will be –9.9 ms⁻¹ (same magnitude, opposite direction)
[2 marks — 1 for correct number, 1 for correct sign]

Page 11 — Free Fall and Projectile Motion

1)a) You only need to worry about the vertical motion of the stone.
$u = 0$ ms⁻¹, $s = -560$ m, $a = -g = -9.81$ ms⁻², $t = ?$
You need to find t, so use: $s = ut + \frac{1}{2}at^2$ [1 mark]
$-560 = 0 + \frac{1}{2} \times -9.81 \times t^2$

$t = \sqrt{\dfrac{2 \times (-560)}{-9.81}} = 10.7\,s$ (1 d.p.) $= 11$ s (to the nearest second)

[1 mark]

b) You know that in the horizontal direction:
$v = 20$ m/s, $t = 10.7$ s, $a = 0$, $s = ?$

So use velocity $= \dfrac{distance}{time}$, $v = \dfrac{s}{t}$ [1 mark]

$s = v \times t = 20 \times 10.7 = 214$ m (to the nearest metre) [1 mark]

2) You know that for the arrow's vertical motion (taking upwards as the positive direction):
$a = -9.81$ ms⁻², $u = 30$ ms⁻¹ and the arrow will be at its highest point just before it starts falling back towards the ground, so $v = 0$ m/s.
$s = $ the distance travelled from the arrow's firing point
So use $v^2 = u^2 + 2as$ [1 mark]
$0 = 30^2 + 2 \times -9.81 \times s$

$900 = 2 \times 9.81s$

$s = \dfrac{900}{2 \times 9.81} = 45.9$ m [1 mark]

So the maximum distance reached from the ground
$= 45.9 + 1 = 47$ m (to the nearest metre). [1 mark]

Page 13 — Displacement-Time Graphs

1) Split graph into four sections:

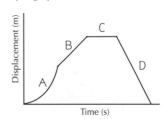

Answers

A: acceleration [1 mark]
B: constant velocity [1 mark]
C: stationary [1 mark]
D: constant velocity in opposite direction to A and B [1 mark]

2)a)
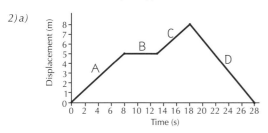

[4 marks — 1 mark for each section correctly drawn]

b) At A: $v = \dfrac{displacement}{time} = \dfrac{5}{8} = 0.625\ ms^{-1}$

At B: $v = 0$

At C: $v = \dfrac{displacement}{time} = \dfrac{3}{5} = 0.6\ ms^{-1}$

At D: $v = \dfrac{displacement}{time} = \dfrac{-8}{10} = -0.8\ ms^{-1}$

[2 marks for all correct or just 1 mark for 2 or 3 correct]

Page 15 — Velocity-Time Graphs
1)a)
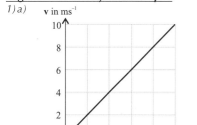

[2 marks]

b) use $s = ut + \frac{1}{2}at^2$ *[1 mark]*
$t = 1, s = 1$
$t = 2, s = 4$
$t = 3, s = 9$
$t = 4, s = 16$
$t = 5, s = 25$
[2 marks for all correct or 1 mark for at least 3 pairs of values right]

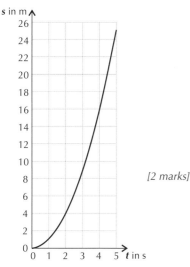

[2 marks]

c) *E.g. another way to calculate displacement is to find the area under the velocity-time graph. [1 mark]*
E.g. total displacement = ½ × 5 ×10 = 25 m [1 mark]

Page 17 — Mass, Weight and Centre of Gravity
1)a) *Density is a measure of 'compactness' of a material — its mass per unit volume. [1 mark]*
b) $\rho = \dfrac{m}{V}$ *[1 mark]*

V of cylinder $= \pi r^2 h = \pi \times 4^2 \times 6 = 301.6\ cm^3$ *[1 mark]*
$\rho = 820 \div 301.6 = 2.72\ g\,cm^{-3}$ *[1 mark]*
c) $V = 5 \times 5 \times 5 = 125\ cm^3$
$m = \rho \times V = 2.7 \times 125 = 340\ g$ *[1 mark]*
2) *Experiment:*
Hang the object freely from a point. Hang a plumb bob from the same point, and use it to draw a vertical line down the object. [1 mark]
Repeat for a different point and find the point of intersection. [1 mark]
The centre of gravity is halfway through the thickness of the object (by symmetry) at the point of intersection.
Identifying and reducing error, e.g.:
Source: the object and/or plumb line might move slightly while you're drawing the vertical line [1 mark]
Reduced by: hang the object from a third point to confirm the position of the point of intersection [1 mark]

Page 19 — Forces
1)
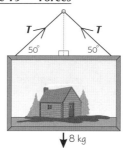

Weight = vertical component of tension × 2
$8 \times 9.81 = 2T \sin 50°$ *[1 mark]*
$78.48 = 0.766 \times 2T$
$102.45 = 2T$
$T = 51.2\ N$ *[1 mark]*
2)
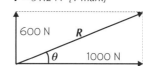

By Pythagoras:
$R = \sqrt{1000^2 + 600^2} = 1166\ N$ *[1 mark]*

$\tan\theta = \dfrac{600}{1000}$ *, so* $\theta = \tan^{-1} 0.6 = 31.0°$ *[1 mark]*

Page 21 — Moments and Torques
1) *Torque = Force × distance [1 mark]*
$60 = 0.4F$*, so* $F = 150\ N$ *[1 mark]*
2)
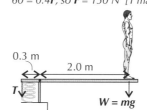

clockwise moment = anticlockwise moment
$W \times 2.0 = T \times 0.3$ *[1 mark for either line of working]*
$60 \times 9.81 \times 2.0 = T \times 0.3$
$T = 3924\ N$ *[1 mark]*
The tension in the spring is equal and opposite to the force exerted by the diver on the spring.

Answers

Page 23 — Newton's Laws of Motion

1)a)

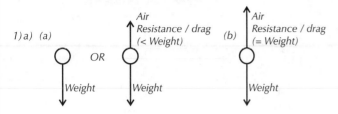

(a) OR
(a) Air Resistance / drag (< Weight) — Weight
(b) Air Resistance / drag (= Weight) — Weight

[1 mark for each diagram]

2)a) *Force perpendicular to river flow = 500 − 100 = 400 N [1 mark]*
   Force parallel to river flow = 300 N

   Resultant force = $\sqrt{400^2 + 300^2}$ = 500 N [1 mark]

   b) *$a = F/m$ (from $F = ma$) [1 mark]*
   = 500/250 = 2 ms^{-2} [1 mark]

3)a) *The resultant force acting on it [1 mark] and its mass. [1 mark]*
   b) *Michael is able to exert a greater force than Tom.*
   Michael is lighter than Tom. [1 mark each for 2 sensible points]
   c) *The only force acting on each of them is their weight = mg [1 mark]. Since $F = ma$, this gives $ma = mg$, or $a = g$ [1 mark]. Their acceleration doesn't depend on their mass — it's the same for both of them — so they reach the water at the same time. [1 mark]*

Page 25 — Terminal Velocity

1)a) *The velocity increases at a steady rate, which means the acceleration is constant. [1 mark]*
   Constant acceleration means there must be no atmospheric resistance (atmospheric resistance would increase with velocity, leading to a decrease in acceleration). So there must be no atmosphere. [1 mark]

   b) velocity

   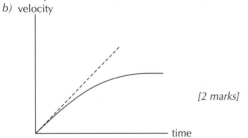

   [2 marks]

   time

   Your graph must be a smooth curve which levels out. It must NOT go down at the end.
   c) *(The graph becomes less steep)*
   because the acceleration is decreasing [1 mark]
   because air resistance increases with speed [1 mark]
   (The graph levels out)
   because air resistance has become equal to weight [1 mark]
   If the question says 'explain', you won't get marks for just describing what the graph shows — you have to say <u>why</u> it is that shape.

Page 27 — Forces on Vehicles and Car Safety

1)a) *reaction time is 0.5 s, speed is 20 ms^{-1}*
   $s = vt$ [1 mark]
   = 20 × 0.5 = 10 m [1 mark]
   b) *Use $F = ma$ to get a: $a = -10\,000/850 = -11.76$ ms^{-2} [1 mark]*

   Use $v^2 = u^2 + 2as$, and rearrange to get $s = \dfrac{v^2 - u^2}{2a}$

   Put in the values: $s = (0 - 400) \div (2 \times -11.76)$ [1 mark]
   = 17 m [1 mark]
   Remember that a force against the direction of motion is negative.
   c) *Total stopping distance = 10 + 17 = 27 m*
   She stops 3 m before the cow. [1 mark]

2)a) *Car: use $v = u + at$ to get acceleration:*
   $a = (0 - 20)/0.1 = -200$ ms^{-2} [1 mark]
   Use $F = ma$:
   $F = 900 \times -200 = -180\,000$ N [1 mark]
   Same for dummy:
   $a = 0 - 18/0.1 = -180$ ms^{-2} [1 mark]
   $F = 50 \times -180 = -9000$ N [1 mark]
   b) *Crumple zones will increase the collision time for the car and dummy;*
   this reduces forces on the car and dummy;
   the airbag will keep the dummy in its seat;
   and increase the collision time further for the dummy;
   reducing the force on it.
   [3 marks for any three sensible points]

Page 29 — Work and Power

1)a)

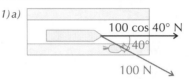

100 cos 40° N
40°
100 N

   Force in direction of travel = 100 cos40° = 76.6 N [1 mark]
   $W = Fs$ = 76.6 × 1500 = 114 900 J [1 mark]
   b) *Use $P = Fv$ [1 mark]*
   = 100 cos40° × 0.8 = 61.3 W [1 mark]
2)a) *Use $W = Fs$ [1 mark]*
   = 20 × 9.81 × 3 = 588.6 J [1 mark]
   Remember that 20 kg is not the force — it's the mass. So you need to multiply it by 9.81 Nkg^{-1} to get the weight.
   b) *Use $P = Fv$ [1 mark]*
   = 20 × 9.81 × 0.25 = 49.05 W [1 mark]

Page 31 — Conservation of Energy

1)a) *Use $E_k = \frac{1}{2}mv^2$ and $E_p = mgh$ [1 mark]*
   $\frac{1}{2}mv^2 = mgh$
   $\frac{1}{2}v^2 = gh$
   $v^2 = 2gh = 2 \times 9.81 \times 2 = 39.24$ [1 mark]
   $v = 6.26$ ms^{-1} [1 mark]
   'No friction' allows you to say that the changes in kinetic and potential energy will be the same.
   b) *2 m — no friction means the kinetic energy will all change back into potential energy, so he will rise back up to the same height as he started. [1 mark]*
   c) *Put in some more energy by actively 'skating'. [1 mark]*
2)a) *If there's no air resistance, $E_k = E_p = mgh$ [1 mark]*
   $E_k = 0.02 \times 9.81 \times 8 = 1.57$ J [1 mark]
   b) *If the ball rebounds to 6.5 m, it has gravitational potential energy:*
   $E_p = mgh = 0.02 \times 9.81 \times 6.5 = 1.28$ J [1 mark]
   So 1.57 − 1.28 = 0.29 J is converted to other forms [1 mark]

Section Two — Materials
Page 33 — Hooke's Law

1)a) *Force is proportional to extension.*
   The force is 1.5 times as great, so the extension will also be 1.5 times the original value.
   Extension = 1.5 × 4.0 mm = 6.0 mm [1 mark]
   b) *$F = ke$ and so $k = F/e$ [1 mark]*
   $k = 10 \div 4.0 \times 10^{-3} = 2500$ Nm^{-1} (or 2.5 Nmm^{-1}) [1 mark]
   There is one mark for rearranging the equation and another for getting the right numerical answer.
   c) *One mark for any sensible point e.g.*
   The string now stretches much further for small increases in force.
   When the string is loosened it is longer than at the start. [1 mark]

Answers

2) The rubber band does not obey Hooke's law *[1 mark]* because when the force is doubled from 2.5 N to 5 N, the extension increases by a factor of 2.3. *[1 mark]*

Page 35 — Stress and Strain
1)a) Area = $\pi d^2/4$ or πr^2.
So area = $\pi \times (1 \times 10^{-3})^2/4 = 7.85 \times 10^{-7}$ m^2 *[1 mark]*
b) Stress = force/area = $300/(7.85 \times 10^{-7})$
$= 3.82 \times 10^8$ Nm^{-2} or Pa *[1 mark]*
c) Strain = extension/length = $4 \times 10^{-3}/2.00 = 2 \times 10^{-3}$ *[1 mark]*
2)a) $F = ke$ and so rearranging $k = F/e$ *[1 mark]*
So $k = 50/(3.0 \times 10^{-3}) = 1.67 \times 10^4$ Nm^{-1} *[1 mark]*
b) Elastic strain energy = $\frac{1}{2}Fe$
Giving the elastic strain energy as
$\frac{1}{2} \times 50 \times 3 \times 10^{-3} = 7.5 \times 10^{-2}$ J *[1 mark]*
3) Elastic strain energy,
$E = \frac{1}{2}ke^2 = \frac{1}{2} \times 40.8 \times 0.05^2 = 0.051$ J *[1 mark]*
To find maximum speed, assume all this energy is converted to kinetic energy in the ball. $E_{kinetic} = E$ *[1 mark]*
$E = \frac{1}{2}mv^2$, so rearranging, $v^2 = 2E/m$ *[1 mark]*
$v^2 = (2 \times 0.051)/0.012 = 8.5$, so $v = 2.92$ ms^{-1} *[1 mark]*

Page 37 — The Young Modulus
1)a) Cross-sectional area = $\pi d^2/4$ or πr^2.
So the cross-sectional area = $\pi \times (0.6 \times 10^{-3})^2/4 = 2.83 \times 10^{-7}$ m^2 *[1 mark]*
b) Stress = force/area = $80/(2.83 \times 10^{-7}) = 2.83 \times 10^8$ Nm^{-2} *[1 mark]*
c) Strain = extension/length = $3.6 \times 10^{-3}/2.5 = 1.44 \times 10^{-3}$ *[1 mark]*
d) The Young modulus for steel = stress/strain
$= 2.83 \times 10^8/(1.44 \times 10^{-3}) = 2.0 \times 10^{11}$ Nm^{-2} *[1 mark]*
2)a) The Young modulus, E = stress/strain and so strain = stress/E *[1 mark]*
Strain on copper = $2.6 \times 10^8/1.3 \times 10^{11} = 2 \times 10^{-3}$ *[1 mark]*
There's one mark for rearranging the equation and another for using it.
b) Stress = force/area and so area = force/stress
Area of the wire = $100/(2.6 \times 10^8) = 3.85 \times 10^{-7}$ m^2 *[1 mark]*
c) Strain energy per unit volume = $\frac{1}{2} \times$ stress $\times$ strain
$= \frac{1}{2} \times 2.6 \times 10^8 \times 2 \times 10^{-3} = 2.6 \times 10^5$ Jm^{-3} *[1 mark]*
Give the mark if answer is consistent with the value calculated for strain in part a).

Page 39 — Structure of Solids
1) One mark for any composite material, one mark for a sensible application of that material, and one further mark for any sensible advantage of this material, e.g. reinforced concrete used in construction is stronger under tension than standard concrete; fibre-reinforced plastic (fibreglass) used in kayaks has a greater resistance to compressive and tensile forces than the plastic alone. *[3 marks]*
2) The height of the image is approximately 13.5 atoms. *[1 mark]*
So the size of each atom is $4.05 \div 13.5 = 0.3$ nm. *[1 mark]*

Page 42 — Behaviour of Solids
1)a) A hard material is resistant to cutting, indentation and abrasion. *[1 mark]*
Brittle materials break suddenly without deforming plastically. *[1 mark]*
b) One mark for any sensible use e.g. a cutting instrument. *[1 mark]*
One further mark for an explanation relating the use to the properties of hardened steel e.g. because the instrument would be able to cut through surfaces without getting damaged itself. *[1 mark]*

c)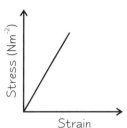
[1 mark for correctly labelled axes, 1 mark for straight line through the origin]
2) E.g. The material would need to be stiff *[1 mark]* so that it would keep its shape and not crush the rider's head when a force was applied to it. *[1 mark]* It would also need to be tough *[1 mark]* so that it could absorb the energy of an impact without breaking. *[1 mark]* The material should be lightweight / have a low density *[1 mark]* so that it is comfortable for the rider to wear. *[1 mark]*

Page 45 — Properties of Fluids
1)a)
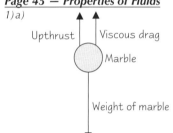

[1 mark for each force correctly drawn and labelled]
b) The resultant force is zero. *[1 mark]*
c) Weight of marble = $mg = 5 \times 10^{-5} \times 9.81 = 4.9 \times 10^{-4}$ N *[1 mark]*
Weight of displaced water = mg
$= 2.1 \times 10^{-5} \times 9.81 = 2.1 \times 10^{-4}$ N
Upthrust = weight of displaced water = 2.1×10^{-4} N *[1 mark]*
Viscous drag (F) + upthrust – weight of marble = 0 N *[1 mark]*
Viscous drag = weight of marble – upthrust
$= 4.9 \times 10^{-4} – 2.1 \times 10^{-4} = 2.8 \times 10^{-4}$ N *[1 mark]*
Stoke's law states $F = 6\pi\eta rv$. Rearranging, $v = F \div (6\pi\eta r)$ *[1 mark]*
$v = 2.8 \times 10^{-4} \div [6 \times \pi \times 0.0011 \times (5 \times 10^{-3})] = 2.7$ ms^{-1} *[1 mark]*
2) Oil flows more slowly during the night because nights tend to be colder than days *[1 mark]*. The lower temperature means that the viscosity of the fuel is greater at night *[1 mark]*, which in turn means that its rate of flow is slower than in the day *[1 mark]*.

Section Three — Electricity
Page 47 — Charge, Current and Potential Difference
1) Time in seconds = $10 \times 60 = 600$ s.
Use the formula $I = Q / t$ *[1 mark]*
which gives you $I = 4500 / 600 = 7.5$ A *[1 mark]*
Write down the formula first. Don't forget the unit in your answer.
2) Rearrange the formula $I = nAvq$ and you get $v = I / nAq$ *[1 mark]*
which gives you
$v = \dfrac{13}{(1.0 \times 10^{29}) \times (5.0 \times 10^{-6}) \times (1.6 \times 10^{-19})}$ *[1 mark]*
$v = 1.63 \times 10^{-4}$ ms^{-1} *[1 mark]*
3) Work done = $0.75 \times$ electrical energy input
so the energy input will be $90 / 0.75 = 120$ J. *[1 mark]*
Rearrange the formula $V = W / Q$ to give $Q = W / V$ *[1 mark]*
so you get $Q = 120 / 12 = 10$ C. *[1 mark]*
The electrical energy input to a motor has to be greater than the work it does because motors are less than 100% efficient.

Answers

Page 49 — Resistance and Conductance
1)a) Area = $\pi(d/2)^2$ and $d = 1.0 \times 10^{-3}$ m
so Area = $\pi \times (0.5 \times 10^{-3})^2 = 7.85 \times 10^{-7}$ m² [1 mark]

$$R = \frac{\rho l}{A} = \frac{2.8 \times 10^{-8} \times 4}{7.85 \times 10^{-7}} = 0.14\ \Omega$$

[1 mark for equation or working, 1 mark for answer with unit.]
b) Resistance will now be zero [1 mark]
Because aluminium is a superconductor below its transition temperature of 1.2 K [1 mark]
2)a) $R = V / I$ [1 mark]

$$= \frac{2}{2.67 \times 10^{-3}} = 749\ \Omega \quad [1\ mark]$$

b) Two further resistance calculations give 750 Ω for each answer [1 mark]
There is no significant change in resistance for different potential differences [1 mark]
Component is an ohmic conductor because its resistance is constant for different potential differences. [1 mark]

Page 51 — I/V Characteristics
1)a)

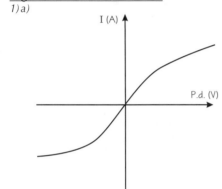

[1 mark]
b) Resistance increases as the temperature increases [1 mark]
c) Increase in temperature makes metal ions vibrate more [1 mark]
Increased collisions with ions impedes electrons [1 mark]

Page 53 — Electrical Energy, Power and Fuses
1)a) $I = P/V$ [1 mark] = 920/230 = 4 A [1 mark]
b) $I = V/R$ [1 mark] = 230/190 = 1.21 A [1 mark]
c) $P_{motor} = VI = 230 \times 1.21 = 278$ W [1 mark]
Total power = motor power + heater power
= 278 + 920 = 1198 W, which is approx. 1.2 kW [1 mark]
d) Energy = power × time = 1.2 × 0.25 = 0.3 kWh. [1 mark]
2)a) Energy supplied = VIt = 12 × 48 × 2 = 1152 J [1 mark]
b) Energy lost = I^2Rt [1 mark] = 48² × 0.01 × 2 = 46 J [1 mark]

Page 55 — E.m.f. and Internal Resistance
1)a) Total resistance = $R + r$ = 4 + 0.8 = 4.8 Ω [1 mark]
I = e.m.f./total resistance = 24/4.8 = 5 A [1 mark]
b) $V = \mathcal{E} - Ir$ = 24 − 5 × 0.8 = 20 V [1 mark]
2)a) $\mathcal{E} = I(R + r)$, so $r = \mathcal{E}/I - R$ [1 mark]
r = 500/(50 × 10⁻³) − 10 = 9990 Ω [1 mark]
b) This is a very high internal resistance [1 mark]
So only small currents can be drawn, reducing the risk to the user [1 mark]

Page 57 — Conservation of Energy & Charge in Circuits
1)a) Resistance of parallel resistors:
$1/R_{parallel}$ = 1/6 + 1/3 = 1/2
$R_{parallel}$ = 2 Ω [1 mark]
Total resistance:
R_{total} = 4 + $R_{parallel}$ = 4 + 2 = 6 Ω [1 mark]
b) $V = IR$, so rearranging $I_3 = V / R_{total}$ [1 mark]
I_3 = 12 / 6 = 2 A [1 mark]
c) $V = IR$ = 2 × 4 = 8 V [1 mark]
d) E.m.f. = sum of p.d.s in circuit, so 12 = 8 + $V_{parallel}$
$V_{parallel}$ = 12 − 8 = 4 V [1 mark]
e) Current = p.d. / resistance
I_1 = 4 / 3 = 1.33 A [1 mark]
I_2 = 4 / 6 = 0.67 A [1 mark]

Page 59 — The Potential Divider
1) Parallel circuit, so p.d. across both sets of resistors is 12 V.
a) V_{AB} = ½ × 12 = 6 V [1 mark]
b) V_{AC} = 2/3 × 12 = 8 V [1 mark]
c) $V_{BC} = V_{AC} - V_{AB}$ = 8 − 6 = 2 V [1 mark]
2)a) V_{AB} = 50/80 × 12 = 7.5 V [1 mark]
(ignore the 10 Ω — no current flows that way)
b) Total resistance of the parallel circuit:
$1/R_T$ = 1/50 + 1/(10 + 40) = 1/25
R_T = 25Ω [1 mark]
p.d. over the whole parallel arrangement = 25/55 × 12 = 5.45 V [1 mark]
p.d. across AB = 40/50 × 5.45 = 4.36 V [1 mark]
current through 40 Ω resistor = V/R = 4.36/40 = 0.11 A [1 mark]

Page 61 — Alternating Current
1)

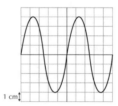

$T = 1 / f$ = 1/100 = 0.01 s (10 ms) [1 mark]
Length of wave on screen = T / time base
= 10 ms / 2 ms cm⁻¹ = 5 cm.
So, one wave occupies 5 cm horizontally and two waves take up the whole screen. [1 mark]
Height of wave on screen = peak voltage / voltage sensitivity
= 2 V / 0.5 V cm⁻¹ = 4 cm.
Therefore the wave peaks 4 cm above the zero line and reaches its lowest value 4 cm below the zero line [1 mark]
[Plus 1 mark for drawing the diagram correctly]
2)a)

A d.c. signal produces a horizontal straight line. [1 mark]
Trace is a straight line 2 divs above the zero line. [1 mark]
b)

f = 50 Hz so T = 1 / 50 = 20 ms. [1 mark]
20 ms / 5 ms div⁻¹ = 4 divs, one wave occupies 4 divisions [1 mark]
The height is 1½ divs above and below, vertically. [1 mark]

3)a) **T** = 1/2500 = 4 × 10⁻⁴ s = 0.4 ms *[1 mark]*

b) One complete wave must occupy 2 divisions if five waves are seen on the whole screen. *[1 mark]*
2 divisions represents a time of 0.4 ms.
So the time-base setting is 0.2 ms per division or 2 × 10⁻⁴ s per division *[1 mark]*

Section Four — Imaging and Signalling

Page 63 — The Nature of Waves

1)a) Use **v** = **λf** and **f** = 1 / **T**
So **v** = **λ** / **T** , giving **λ** = **vT** *[1 mark]*
λ = 3 ms⁻¹ × 6 s = 18 m *[1 mark]*
The vertical movement of the buoy is irrelevant to this part of the question.

b) The trough to peak distance is twice the amplitude, so the amplitude is 0.6 m *[1 mark]*

Page 65 — Longitudinal and Transverse Waves

1)a) *[This question could equally well be answered using diagrams.]*
For ordinary light, the EM field vibrates in all planes at right angles to the direction of travel. *[1 mark]*
Iceland spar acts as a polariser. *[1 mark]*
When light is shone through the first disc, it only allows through vibrations in one particular plane, so emerges less bright. *[1 mark]*
As the two crystals are rotated relative to each other there comes a point when the allowed planes are at right angles to each other. *[1 mark]*
So all the light is blocked. *[1 mark]*
Try to remember to say that for light and other EM waves it's the electric and magnetic <u>fields</u> that vibrate.

b) Using Malus' law, $I = I_0 \cos^2 \sigma$. I is half the size of I_0, so $I/I_0 = 0.5$. Which means $\cos^2\sigma = 0.5$, so $\cos\sigma = 0.707...$ and $\sigma = 45°$

2) E.g. Polarising filters are used in photography to remove unwanted reflections *[1 mark]*. Light is partially polarised when it reflects so putting a polarising filter over the lens at 90 degrees to the plane of polarisation will block most of the reflected light. *[1 mark]*.

Page 67 — Ultrasound Imaging

1)a)

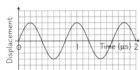

The graph should have a shorter wavelength and lower amplitude than the original. *[1 mark]*

b)

The graph should have a longer wavelength and lower amplitude than the original. *[1 mark]*

2) Any two of, e.g. It will be very expensive and the money could be better spent on development in technologies that would have a more immediate benefit. / The trip will have a huge psychological and physiological effect on the astronauts involved. / Space missions have a very high risk of fatality for the astronauts.
[1 mark for describing an issue, 1 mark for explaining it — to a maximum of 4 marks]

Page 69 — The Electromagnetic Spectrum

1) At the same speed. *[1 mark]*
Both are electromagnetic waves and hence travel at **c**, the speed of light in a vacuum. *[1 mark]*

2)a) Medical X-rays *[1 mark]* rely on the fact that X-rays penetrate the body well but are blocked by bone. *[1 mark]*
OR
Security scanners at airports *[1 mark]* rely on the fact that X-rays penetrate suitcases and clothes but are blocked by metal e.g. of a weapon. *[1 mark]*

b) The main difference between gamma rays and X-rays is that gamma rays arise from nuclear decay *[1 mark]* but X-rays are generated when metals are bombarded with electrons. *[1 mark]*

3) Any of: unshielded microwaves, excess heat, damage to eyes from too bright light, sunburn or skin cancer from UV, cancer or eye damage due to ionisation by X-rays or gamma rays.
[1 mark for the type of EM wave, 1 mark for the danger to health]

Page 71 — Information in Images

1)a)

The diagram should show a fairly uniform mid-grey outside, with a lighter square in the centre. *[1 mark]*

b) Noise can be removed by replacing each pixel with the median of itself and the eight pixels surrounding it. *[1 mark]*

c)

100	99	100
97	100	98
101	101	98

[1 mark]

2)a) Number of bits = $\log_2(65\ 536)$ = 16 *[1 mark]*

b) 16 ÷ 8 = 2 bytes *[1 mark]*

Page 73 — Sampling

1) $b = \log_2\left(\dfrac{V_{total}}{V_{noise}}\right) = \log_2\left(\dfrac{160}{10}\right) = \log_2 16 = \textbf{4 bits}$ *[2 marks for the correct answer, otherwise 1 mark for some correct working]*

2) Minimum sampling rate = 2 × maximum frequency
= 2 × 500 = **1000 samples per second** *[1 mark]*

Page 75 — Signal Spectra and Bandwidth

1)a) Rate of transmission = samples per second × bits per sample
= 8000 × 8 = **64 000 bits per second** *[1 mark]*

b) 1 byte = 8 bits.
So, 64 000 bits per second = **8000 bytes per second**. *[1 mark]*

2)a) All the frequencies that make up the signal and their relative strengths. *[1 mark]*

b) 1400 − 200 = **1200 Hz** *[1 mark]*

Page 77 — Forming Images with Lenses

1)a) Rays meeting the lens parallel to the principal axis converge at the focal point. / Waves parallel to the lens axis are given spherical curvature as they pass through the lens. This curvature is centred on the focal point. *[1 mark]*
The focal length is the distance between the lens axis and the principal focus *[1 mark]*.

b) $\dfrac{1}{v} = \dfrac{1}{u} + \dfrac{1}{f}$ so $\dfrac{1}{v} = -\dfrac{1}{0.2} + \dfrac{1}{0.15} = \dfrac{5}{3} \Rightarrow$ **v = 0.6 m** *[1 mark]*

Answers

2)a) $m = \dfrac{\text{size of image}}{\text{size of object}} = \dfrac{47.2}{12.5} = 3.776$ *[1 mark]*

b) $m = \dfrac{v}{u}$, giving $v = m \times u$ *[1 mark]*

$v = 3.776 \times 4 = 15.1$ mm *[1 mark]*

c) $P = \dfrac{1}{f} = \dfrac{1}{v} - \dfrac{1}{u}$, so $P = \dfrac{1}{15.1} - \left(-\dfrac{1}{4}\right) = 0.316$ D

Remember u is negative.

[3 marks for the correct answer, otherwise 1 mark for stating the correct equation and 1 further mark for some correct working]

Section Five — Wave Phenomena
Page 79 — Refractive Index
1)a) $n_{diamond} = c / v_{diamond} = (3 \times 10^8) / (1.24 \times 10^8) = 2.42$ *[1 mark]*

b) $n_{air} \sin i = n_{diamond} \sin r$, $n_{air} = 1$
So, $n_{diamond} = \sin i / \sin r$ *[1 mark]*

$\sin r = \dfrac{\sin i}{n_{diamond}} = \dfrac{\sin 50}{2.42} = 0.317$

$r = 18.5°$ *[1 mark]*

You can assume the refractive index of air is 1, and don't forget to write the degree sign in your answer.

2)a) *When the light is pointing steeply upwards some of it is refracted and some reflected — the beam emerging from the surface is the refracted part. [1 mark]*
However when the beam hits the surface at more than the critical angle (to the normal to the boundary) refraction does not occur. All the beam is totally internally reflected to light the tank, hence its brightness. [1 mark]

b) *The critical angle is 90° – 41.25° = 48.75°. [1 mark]*
$n_{water} = 1 / \sin C$
$= 1 / \sin 48.75°$
$= 1 / 0.752 = 1.33$ *[1 mark]*

The question talks about the angle between the light beam and the floor of the aquarium. This angle is 90° minus the incident angle — measured from a normal to the surface of the water.

Page 81 — Superposition and Coherence
1)a) *The frequencies and wavelengths of the two sources must be equal [1 mark] and the phase difference must be constant. [1 mark]*

b) *Interference will only be noticeable if the amplitudes of the two waves are approximately equal. [1 mark]*

2)a) *180° (or 180° + 360n°). [1 mark]*

b) *The displacements and velocities of the two points are equal in size [1 mark] but in opposite directions. [1 mark]*

Page 83 — Stationary (Standing) Waves
1)a)

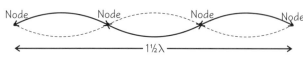

[1 mark for the correct shape, 1 mark for labelling the length]

b) *For a string vibrating at three times the fundamental frequency,*
length = $3\lambda / 2$
$1.2 \text{ m} = 3\lambda / 2$
$\lambda = 0.8$ m *[1 mark]*

c) *When the string forms a standing wave, its amplitude varies from a maximum at the antinodes to zero at the nodes. [1 mark] In a progressive wave all the points have the same amplitude. [1 mark]*

Page 85 — Diffraction
1) *When a wavefront meets an obstacle, the waves will diffract round the corners of the obstacle. When the obstacle is much bigger than the wavelength, little diffraction occurs. In this case, the mountain is much bigger than the wavelength of short-wave radio. So the "shadow" where you cannot pick up short wave is very long. [1 mark]*

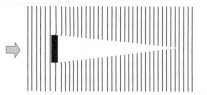

[1 mark]

When the obstacle is comparable in size to the wavelength, as it is for the long-wave radio waves, more diffraction occurs. The wavefront re-forms after a shorter distance, leaving a shorter "shadow". [1 mark]

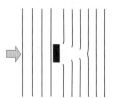

[1 mark]

Page 87 — Two-Source Interference
1)a)

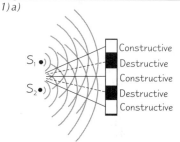

[1 mark for correct constructive interference patterns,
1 mark for correct destructive interference patterns]

b) *Light waves from separate sources are not coherent, as light is emitted in random bursts of energy. To get coherent light the two sets of waves must emerge from one source. [1 mark] A laser is used because it emits coherent light that is all of one wavelength. [1 mark]*

2)a) $\lambda = v / f = 330 / 1320 = 0.25$ m. *[1 mark]*

b) *Separation = $X = \lambda D / d$ [1 mark]*
$= 0.25 \text{ m} \times 7 \text{ m} / 1.5 \text{ m} = 1.17$ m. *[1 mark]*

Page 89 — Diffraction Gratings
1)a) *Use $\sin \theta = n\lambda / d$*
For the first order, $n = 1$
So, $\sin \theta = \lambda / d$ [1 mark]
No need to actually work out d. The number of lines per metre is 1 / d. So you can simply multiply the wavelength by that.
$\sin \theta = 600 \times 10^{-9} \times 4 \times 10^5 = 0.24$
$\theta = 13.9°$ *[1 mark]*
For the second order, $n = 2$ and $\sin \theta = 2\lambda / d$. [1 mark]
You already have a value for λ / d. Just double it to get $\sin \theta$ for the second order.
$\sin \theta = 0.48$
$\theta = 28.7°$ *[1 mark]*

b) *No. Putting $n = 5$ into the equation gives a value of $\sin \theta$ of 1.2, which is impossible. [1 mark]*

2) $\sin \theta = n\lambda / d$, *so for the 1st order maximum, $\sin \theta = \lambda / d$ [1 mark]*
$\sin 14.2° = \lambda \times 3.7 \times 10^5$
$\lambda = 663$ nm (or 6.63×10^{-7} m) *[1 mark].*

Answers

Section Six — Quantum Phenomena

Page 91 — Light — Wave or Particle

1)a) At threshold voltage: $E_{kinetic}$ of an electron = E_{photon} emitted [1 mark]
So E_{photon} = e × V = 1.6 × 10^{-19} × 1.7 = 2.72 × 10^{-19} J [1 mark]

b) $E = \dfrac{hc}{\lambda}$ [1 mark], so $h = \dfrac{E\lambda}{c}$

$\lambda = 7.0 \times 10^{-7}$ m, $c = 3.0 \times 10^8$ ms^{-1},

So, $h = \dfrac{2.72 \times 10^{-19} \times 7.0 \times 10^{-7}}{3.0 \times 10^8} = 6.3 \times 10^{-34}$ Js [1 mark]

Page 93 — The Photoelectric Effect

1) $\phi = 2.9$ eV $= 2.9 \times (1.6 \times 10^{-19})$ J $= 4.64 \times 10^{-19}$ J [1 mark]

$f = \dfrac{\phi}{h} = \dfrac{4.64 \times 10^{-19}}{6.6 \times 10^{-34}} = 7.0 \times 10^{14}$ Hz (to 2 s.f.) [1 mark]

2)a) $E = hf$ [1 mark]

$= (6.6 \times 10^{-34}) \times (2.0 \times 10^{15}) = 1.32 \times 10^{-18}$ J [1 mark]

1.32×10^{-18} J $= \dfrac{1.32 \times 10^{-18}}{1.6 \times 10^{-19}}$ eV $= 8.25$ eV [1 mark]

b) $E_{max\ kinetic} = E_{photon} - \phi = 8.25 - 4.7 = 3.55$ eV (or 5.68×10^{-19} J) [1 mark]

3) An electron needs to gain a certain amount of energy (the work function energy) before it can leave the surface of the metal (to overcome the bonds holding it to the metal). [1 mark]
If the energy carried by each photon is less than this work function energy, no electrons will be emitted [1 mark].

Page 95 — Energy Levels and Photon Emission

1)a) i) $E = V = 12.1$ eV [1 mark]
ii) $E = V \times 1.6 \times 10^{-19} = 12.1 \times 1.6 \times 10^{-19} = 1.9 \times 10^{-18}$ J [1 mark]
b) i) The movement of an electron from a lower energy level to a higher energy level by absorbing energy. [1 mark]
ii) $-13.6 + 12.1 = -1.5$ eV. This corresponds to $n = 3$. [1 mark]
iii) $n = 3 \rightarrow n = 2$: $3.4 - 1.5 = 1.9$ eV [1 mark]
$n = 2 \rightarrow n = 1$: $13.6 - 3.4 = 10.2$ eV [1 mark]
$n = 3 \rightarrow n = 1$: $13.6 - 1.5 = 12.1$ eV [1 mark]

Page 97 — Wave-Particle Duality

1)a) Electromagnetic radiation can show characteristics of both a particle and a wave. [1 mark]

b) i) $E_{photon} = \dfrac{hc}{\lambda} = \dfrac{6.63 \times 10^{-34} \times 3.00 \times 10^8}{590 \times 10^{-9}}$ [1 mark]

$= 3.37 \times 10^{-19}$ J [1 mark]

E (in eV) $= \dfrac{E \text{ (in J)}}{1.6 \times 10^{-19}} = \dfrac{3.37 \times 10^{-19}}{1.6 \times 10^{-19}} = 2.11$ eV [1 mark]

ii) $\lambda = \dfrac{h}{mv}$ [1 mark]

$\therefore v = \dfrac{h}{m\lambda} = \dfrac{6.63 \times 10^{-34}}{9.11 \times 10^{-31} \times 590 \times 10^{-9}} = 1230$ ms^{-1} [1 mark]

2)a) $\lambda = \dfrac{h}{mv}$ [1 mark]

$= \dfrac{6.63 \times 10^{-34}}{9.11 \times 10^{-31} \times 3.5 \times 10^6} = 2.08 \times 10^{-10}$ m [1 mark]

b) Either $v = \dfrac{h}{m\lambda}$ with $m_{proton} = 1840 \times m_{electron}$

or momentum of protons = momentum of electrons

$1840 \times \cancel{m_e} \times v_p = \cancel{m_e} \times 3.5 \times 10^6$

$v_p = 1900$ ms^{-1}

[1 mark for either method with correct substitution, 1 mark for correct answer]

c) The two have the same kinetic energy if the voltages are the same. The proton has a larger mass, so it will have a smaller speed. [1 mark] Kinetic energy is proportional to the square of the speed, while momentum is proportional to the speed, so they will have different momenta. [1 mark]
Wavelength depends on the momentum, so the wavelengths are different. [1 mark]
This is a really hard question. If you didn't get it right, make sure you understand the answer fully. Do the algebra if it helps.

3)a) $E_k = 6 \times 10^3$ eV [1 mark]
$= 6000 \times 1.6 \times 10^{-19} = 9.6 \times 10^{-16}$ J [1 mark]

b) $E_k = \dfrac{1}{2}mv^2$ [1 mark]

$9.6 \times 10^{-16} = \dfrac{1}{2} \times 9.11 \times 10^{-31} \times v^2$

$v = \sqrt{\dfrac{2 \times 9.6 \times 10^{-16}}{9.11 \times 10^{-31}}} = 4.6 \times 10^7$ ms^{-1} [1 mark]

c) $\lambda = \dfrac{h}{mv}$ [1 mark]

$= \dfrac{6.63 \times 10^{-34}}{9.11 \times 10^{-31} \times 4.6 \times 10^7} = 1.56 \times 10^{-11}$ m [1 mark]

Page 99 — The "Sum Over Paths" Theory

1) Probability μ (resultant phasor amplitude)^2 [1 mark]
Probability of electron reaching point A μ $(6.3)^2 = 39.69$ [1 mark]
Probability of electron reaching point B μ $(4.5)^2 = 20.25$ [1 mark]
$39.69 , 20.25 = 1.96$, so an electron is almost twice as likely to reach point A as point B. [1 mark]

2) The frequency of phasor rotation = 6.0×10^{14} rotations per second. Use time (s) = distance (m) , speed (ms^{-1}) to find the time taken for the photon to reach the detector.
$t = 0.12 , c = 0.12 , 3.0 \times 10^8 = 4.0 \times 10^{-10}$ s [1 mark]
So the number of phasor rotations along this path
$= f \times t = 6.0 \times 10^{14} \times 4.0 \times 10^{-10} = 2.4 \times 10^5$ rotations [1 mark]

3)a) $E_{kinetic} = \dfrac{1}{2}mv^2$ [1 mark]

$= \dfrac{1}{2} \times 9.1 \times 10^{-31} \times (4.0 \times 10^5)^2 = 7.3 \times 10^{-20}$ J (to 2 s.f.)

[1 mark]

b) $E = hf$ [1 mark]

$f = \dfrac{E}{h} = \dfrac{7.3 \times 10^{-20}}{6.6 \times 10^{-34}} = 1.1 \times 10^{14}$ Hz (to 2.s.f) [1 mark]

Page 101 — Using "Sum Over Paths"

1)a) i) By adding the phasors tip to tail, you can see the resultant is 1 cm long, giving an amplitude of 3. [1 mark]

resultant

ii) All the phasors line up in the same direction, so the resultant is three phasor lengths long, giving a resultant amplitude of $3 \times 3 = 9$. [1 mark]

Answers

b) Probability is proportional to the square of the resultant phasor amplitude. *[1 mark]*
So the probability of a photon reaching point D is nine times greater than the probability of a photon reaching point B. *[1 mark]*

Section Seven — Particles

Page 103 — Atomic Structure

1) Inside every atom there is a nucleus which contains protons and neutrons. *[1 mark]*
Orbiting this core are the electrons. *[1 mark]*
The tiny electrons orbit at comparatively vast distances, so most of the atom is empty space. *[1 mark]*

2) Proton number is 8, so there are 8 protons and 8 electrons. *[1 mark]*
The nucleon number is 16. This is the total number of protons and neutrons.
Subtract the 8 protons and that leaves 8 neutrons. *[1 mark]*

3) Atoms with the same number of protons but different numbers of neutrons are called isotopes. *[1 mark for definition]*
Isotopes have the same chemical reactions and behaviour.
The nuclei have different stabilities.
Isotopes have different physical properties.
[2 marks for any 2 sensible points]

Page 105 — Stable and Unstable Nuclei

1)a) The strong nuclear force must be repulsive at very small nucleon separations to prevent the nucleus being crushed to a point. *[1 mark]*

b) Beyond a few fm the strong nuclear force is smaller than the electrostatic force *[1 mark]*. This means the protons in the nucleus would be forced apart. So a nucleus bigger than this would be unstable *[1 mark]*.

2)a) $^{226}_{88}\text{Ra} \longrightarrow \, ^{222}_{86}\text{Rn} + \, ^{4}_{2}\alpha$

[3 marks available — 1 mark for alpha particle, 1 mark each for proton number and nucleon number of radon]

b) $^{40}_{19}\text{K} \longrightarrow \, ^{40}_{20}\text{Ca} + \, ^{0}_{1}\beta + \overline{\nu}_e$

[4 marks available — 1 mark for beta particle, 1 mark each for proton number and nucleon number of calcium, 1 mark for antineutrino]

Page 107 — Particles and Antiparticles

1) $e^+ + e^- \rightarrow \gamma + \gamma$ *[1 mark]*
This is called annihilation. *[1 mark]*
Remember that there are two photons and they go off in opposite directions, just like two bits from an explosion.

2) The protons, neutrons and electrons which make up the iron atoms would need to annihilate with their antiparticles. *[1 mark]*
No antiparticles are available for this to happen in the iron block. *[1 mark]*

3) The creation of a particle of matter also requires the creation of its antiparticle. In this case no antineutron has been produced. *[1 mark]*

Page 109 — Classification of Particles

1) Proton, electron and electron-antineutrino. *[1 mark]*
The electron and the electron-antineutrino are leptons. *[1 mark]*
Leptons are not affected by the strong interaction, so the decay can't be due to the strong interaction. *[1 mark]*
Remember that this is really just the same as beta decay. Some books might leave out the antineutrino, so don't be misled.

2) Mesons are hadrons but the muon is a lepton. *[1 mark]*
The muon is a fundamental particle but mesons are not.
Mesons are built up from simpler particles. *[1 mark]*
Mesons interact via the strong interaction but the muon does not. *[1 mark]*
You need to classify the muon correctly first and then say why it's different from a meson because of what it's like and what it does.

Page 111 — Quarks

1) $\pi^- = d\overline{u}$ *[1 mark]*
Charge of down quark $= -1/3$ unit.
Charge of anti-up quark $= -2/3$ unit
Total charge $= -1$ unit *[1 mark]*

2) The weak interaction converts a down quark into an up quark plus an electron and an electron-antineutrino. *[1 mark]*
The neutron (udd) becomes a proton (uud). *[1 mark]*
The lepton number L_e is conserved in this reaction.

3) The baryon number changes from 2 to 1, so baryon number is not conserved. *[1 mark]*
The strangeness changes from 0 to 1, so strangeness is not conserved. *[1 mark]*

Page 113 — Exchange Particles and Feynman Diagrams

1) The electrostatic force is due to the exchange of virtual photons that only exist for a very short time. *[1 mark]*
The force is due to the momentum transferred to or gained from the photons as they are emitted or absorbed by a proton. *[1 mark]*

2)

OR

[1 mark for showing a W⁺ boson (or a W⁻ boson) being exchanged in the correct direction, 1 mark for showing a neutron is produced]
This is a weak interaction. *[1 mark]*
Don't forget to put the arrows on your Feynman diagram.
Remember that only the weak interaction can change protons into neutrons or neutrons into protons.

Index

Index